# HOW TO
## SUCCESSFULLY WITH

# PANIC ATTACKS

KAREN SULLIVAN

Wellhouse Publishing Ltd

First published in Great Britain in 2002 by
Wellhouse Publishing Ltd
31 Middle Bourne Lane
Lower Bourne
Farnham
Surrey GU10 3NH

Reprinted in 2003, 2004, 2006, 2009

---

## DISCLAIMER

The aim of this book is to provide general information only and
should not be treated as a substitute for the medical advice of
your doctor or any other health care professional. The publisher
and author are not responsible or liable for any diagnosis made
by a reader based on the contents of this book. Always consult
your doctor if you are in any way concerned about your health.

---

A catalogue record for this book is available from the British Library

ISBN 978-1-903784-08-2


Printed and bound in Ashford Colour Press Ltd., Fareham Road,
Gosport, Hampshire PO13 0FW

For Max

# Contents

# Chapter One

# What Are Panic Attacks?

Panic attacks can occur anywhere, at any time, and often without warning. Some sufferers consider them to be the most terrifying experiences of their lives, while others experience less severe symptoms and are able to pre-empt an attack before it becomes worse.

Whatever the severity of symptoms, however, there is no doubt that panic attacks represent a serious threat to well-being, and compromise quality of life. Because they are so unexpected, and often frightening, they can cause sufferers to avoid any situation where they are likely to occur. For this reason, many people draw back from living full lives, and await the next attack in a state of anticipatory fear.

Most sufferers feel very alone, and are unaware that the symptoms they are experiencing are shared by a multitude of 'normal', healthy people. In the US, for example, some 33 percent of Americans experience a panic attack at some time in their lives. In the UK, the figures are marginally lower, with at least 10 percent of the population suffering a panic attack in any given year – women being between two and three times more likely to experience the problem. New research indicates that one out of every 75 people worldwide will experience a panic attack within their lifetime.

## So What Are Panic Attacks?

Panic attacks comprise part of a syndrome, known as 'panic disorder'. Many people experience just one attack, in which case this isolated incident would not be referred to as a disorder. However, many more people experience random and regular attacks, and would be considered to suffer from panic disorder.

Panic attacks are characterised by a multitude of different symptoms, and they vary between sufferers. Many people experience inexplicable attacks when they feel relatively calm; in fact, a study undertaken by the Panic and Anxiety Hub found that 78 per cent of panic disorder sufferers surveyed reported experiencing a panic attack when relatively 'calm'. Sixty-nine per cent of sufferers reported that attacks came on while going to sleep, while 86 per cent claimed that attacks woke them from sleep at night.

This type of attack is known as 'spontaneous', for obvious reasons. There are, however, a number of forms that a panic attack can take, which means that treatment must be addressed to the individual sufferer rather than offered as a blanket solution for anxiety and anxiety attacks. Let's look at the various types in detail.

The term 'panic disorder' was first recognised and included in the American Psychiatric Association's *Diagnostic & Statistical Manual* (DSM) in 1980. The latest version of the DSM recognises three different types of panic attacks:

*Uncued (Spontaneous) Panic Attacks*
These types of attacks occur without warning, day or night, and in a variety of different situations. They are not induced by a place, a person or a situation, which means that they can be all the more frightening for the sufferer, who may feel as though he or she is dying or having a heart attack (see symptoms, page 10).

*Cued (Specific) Panic Attacks*
These relate to social anxiety disorder, obsessive-compulsive disorder, and post-traumatic stress disorder (PTSD). In other words, a certain situation or place will cause attacks, which means that the sufferer may go to great lengths to avoid it. For example, a person with a social phobia may become agoraphobic because she is unable to face a social situation where she knows she may experience an attack. An obsessive-compulsive may have an overwhelming fear of germs, and suffer an attack in any situation or place where he thinks he may come into contact with them, while a person with PTSD may become anxious and experience a panic attack in a certain situation, or when exposed to a trigger, such as a news report, that reminds him of his initial trauma.

*Situationally Predisposed Panic Attacks*
These are attacks that may occur after exposure to a 'cue' or 'trigger'. In

other words, sufferers may experience panic symptoms in certain situations, but not always. In many ways, these are the most worrying types of attacks, because sufferers never know when they might strike. For example, some people experience panic attacks when driving, or when meeting new people. An attack may occur on one occasion and then not the next. It is often the unpredictability of this type of attack that creates the fear that defines a panic disorder.

In some cases a single spontaneous panic attack, or a handful of them, can lead to a full-blown panic disorder. This in turn can cause secondary conditions associated with panic disorders, which can include avoidance behaviours (such as agoraphobia), depression, or even drug or alcohol abuse, in an attempt to cope.

The important thing to understand is that a panic disorder is driven by fear. Once an initial attack has occurred, the sufferer begins to fear a repeat. It is this fear that creates the scenario for further spontaneous attacks, and even cued or situationally predisposed attacks. The aim is to diagnose and treat the condition early on, to prevent just such an occurrence.

## The Fight or Flight Reaction

The fight or flight response is a natural reaction to danger in humans and in animals. When activated, hormones are released through the body to enable us either to fight the dangerous situation or to run from it. In ancient times it was crucial for humans to be able to deal effectively with threats to their safety, and our bodies are designed to do just that. In the presence of a perceived threat, which might, in the past, have been a bear approaching, or perhaps danger to family or friends, the body begins to release adrenaline.

Adrenaline, also known as epinephrine, is the main stress hormone. It is produced by the two adrenal glands (one above each kidney). When confronted with a stressful situation, blood levels of adrenaline increase by as much as 1,000-fold within one minute. Adrenaline has a dramatic effect on the body. The heart speeds up and the arteries tighten to raise blood pressure. Our livers immediately release emergency stores of glucose into the bloodstream to give us instant energy to fight or run. And digestion shuts down, because the energy necessary for digestion must be diverted elsewhere. The clotting ability of our blood is also increased to prepare for a potential injury. Once we fight or run, the adrenaline is dispersed and levels return to normal.

What does this have to do with panic? A lot. Our thoughts, even those that are subconscious (as in the case of panic attacks that occur during sleep), can 'turn on' the fight or flight response. Our first panic attack may well have been caused by a genuinely frightening or demanding situation that set our fight or flight response into action, but later attacks tend to be a response to the *fear* of having another attack. Our bodies are unable to discern between these thoughts and genuinely dangerous situations. The response is exactly the same.

## Experiencing Panic

One of the worst elements of suffering a panic attack is the feeling of being out of control. Symptoms are not only frightening (often feeling life-threatening), but the experience of being unable to regain composure can be so memorable that many sufferers develop a serious fear of the experience repeating itself.

What happens in a panic attack, and is the experience controllable? Before we look at the symptoms of panic attacks, which vary from sufferer to sufferer, it's important to remember that panic attacks can be controlled, and they can be treated. One of the best ways to do this is to develop an awareness of an impending attack. When the first symptoms begin to kick in, measures can be taken to divert a full-blown panic attack. Once we feel that we are in control, and can control what is going on in our minds and bodies, we are able to halt the process of fear feeding fear, and thus set ourselves on the course to recovery.

The symptoms of a panic attack are described in the DSM as a 'discrete period of intense fear or discomfort in which four (or more) of the following symptoms developed abruptly and reached a peak within 10 minutes':

● palpitations
● pounding heart or accelerated heart rate
● sweating
● trembling or shaking

- sensations of shortness of breath or smothering
- feeling of choking, chest pain or discomfort
- overwhelming need to go to the loo
- feelings of unreality (depersonalisation or derealisation)
- nausea or abdominal distress
- feeling dizzy, unsteady, light-headed or faint
- fear of losing control or going insane, fear of dying
- numbness or tingling sensations
- chills or hot flushes.

A diagnosis of panic disorder is made when a person experiences at least two recurrent, unexpected panic attacks followed by at least one month of fear that another will occur. Frequency of attacks can vary widely. Some people have frequent attacks (for example, every week) that occur for months; others may have clusters of daily attacks followed by weeks or months of remission.

Panic attacks may occur spontaneously or in response to a particular situation. If the person associates fear with circumstances surrounding the original attack, no matter how harmless these circumstances are on their own, then similar circumstances later on may bring back the anxiety, and trigger additional panic attacks.

Panic attacks that include only one or two symptoms, such as dizziness and a pounding heart, are known as limited-symptom attacks; these may be either symptoms left over after a major panic attack or the build-up to a full-blown attack. Panic attacks can also occur with other anxiety disorders, including phobias and post-traumatic stress disorder.

Panic attacks reach maximum intensity within a minute or two of their onset. They diminish slowly – over the next 30 minutes or the next several hours. During the first attack you may feel frightened enough to visit the emergency department of your hospital, or call your doctor. Panic attacks are very frightening, and it's normal to feel great concern for your health and even your life. Subsequent attacks can occur several times a month, and are often as severe as the initial attack.

## Grouping the Symptoms
Experts group the symptoms of panic disorder into six main categories.

## 1. Heart- and Circulation-related
Rapid, irregular or forceful, 'loud' heartbeat; chest pain; low or high blood pressure, often with remarkably wide swings

## 2. Breathing-related
Lowered oxygen level, elevated or lowered carbon dioxide level, under- and over-breathing, sensations of slow suffocation, sensations of inability to take a deep or satisfying breath or to yawn, sensations of abdominal constriction of the lungs, often worse when partially submerged in water

## 3. Muscle-, Skin- and Nerve-related
Jerking, trembling, twitching, spasm, tremor, rigidity, weakness, numbness, tingling, itching, feverishness, chills, hot flushes, 'goose-bumps', excessive or insufficient sweating, hypersensitivity to drugs, flushing, a 'whoosh' sensation

## 4. Digestion-related
Feeling of bile or acid in the throat, heartburn, nausea, vomiting, projectile vomiting, asthma, sinusitis, spasms, burning or aching pain, bleeding, sensitivity to specific foods (triggering gut symptoms or symptoms from any of the other groups listed here), constipation, diarrhoea, incontinence, urinary frequency, excess secretion of bile

## 5. Endocrine-related
Abnormal fluctuations of epinephrine, norepinephrine, insulin, glucagon, renin, aldosterone, cholecystokinin, endorphins and other endocrine substances

## 6. Emotional-Behavioural Expressions
Intense fear, anticipation of impending death, anticipation of imminent fainting (which rarely happens), fear of fleeing, fear of 'going insane', sensations of being outside one's body, sensations of unreality, explosive anger, frequent and escalating anxiety about the next attack, avoidance of situations that have triggered episodes in the past, hypochondria, hypervigilance for sensations or their catastrophic interpretation. Agoraphobia (fear of open spaces) sometimes develops, with patients retreating to smaller and smaller 'safe zones' close to home or sometimes within limited areas of the home.

Panic can have dramatic long- and short-term effects on health, quite apart from the disruption they cause to day-to-day life. Let's look at some of the most common problems.

## Emotional Effects

Fear restricts lifestyle, making it difficult to sustain friendships, make new acquaintances or interact normally socially. The fear of repeated attacks can lead to complete avoidance of normal daily activities and the development of agoraphobia (see page 44).

General anxiety is a common feature of people suffering from panic disorder, which creates irritability, mood swings, tearfulness, physical and emotional exhaustion, feelings of being unable to cope, poor self-esteem and even depression.

Depression is closely linked to anxiety, and very common in people suffering from panic attacks. Panic disorder is a highly debilitating condition that often seems at first glance to have arrived quite suddenly. If untreated, treated unsuccessfully or worsened by misguided treatment, it can lead to acute disability and loss of employment. In many cases, what appears to be depression resolves itself when the underlying panic disorder is successfully treated.

Common symptoms of depression include:
● becoming withdrawn – avoiding friends, family and regular activities
● feeling guilty or bad, being self-critical and self-blaming
● feeling unhappy, miserable and lonely a lot of the time
● feeling hopeless and wanting to die
● difficulty concentrating
● not looking after your personal appearance
● difficulty getting off to sleep or waking very early
● tiredness and lack of energy
● frequent minor health problems such as headaches or stomach-aches.

The risk of suicide in panic attack sufferers is higher than it is in people suffering from depression. Although suicidal patients with anxiety disorders also often have major depression, a recent study on suicide attempts in young adolescents (13 to 14 years old) reported that panic attacks were present in a significant number of those who tried to take their own lives. In many cases, there was no depression present. Other studies report that 25 to 30 per cent of people with panic disorder harbour suicidal thoughts at some point.

*Francesca's Experience*
The worst panic attacks I've had are difficult to distinguish from heart attacks. I remember the first time. I was at home on my own, studying for my university finals which were about a week or so away. Around mid-afternoon I began to feel very sick and realised that a pain in my chest was getting more and more intense. It was like a tight constricting band, making it hard to breathe. I looked in a mirror and my face was pure white. I crawled up to bed and lay still, trying to figure out if I should call an ambulance or not. I knew my dad was coming home in a couple of hours, but I could be dead by then. My shoulder was stiff, my neck was stiff, I felt sick, the tight band round the chest was getting worse, I had breathing difficulties – these are all heart attack symptoms. On the other hand, I was only 21 – surely you don't get heart attacks at that age?

When my dad (who is a doctor) arrived, he checked my pulse, listened to my heart, and said it wasn't a heart attack but that maybe I should take a break from studying for a couple of days. 'I can't,' I shrieked, and then I started to dry retch. My stomach muscles went into spasm and I couldn't stop retching for ages. Dad eventually gave me some kind of tranquilliser, I'm not sure what. I stayed in bed for a day, then went back to studying – and somehow got a double first.

## Physical Effects
The immune system can be compromised by the stress of living in fear of another attack, and by the toll attacks take on the system. Not only are you more likely to be prone to infections, and find them more difficult to fight off, but they may also linger for weeks or even months. It's a vicious circle: illness affects our overall sense of wellbeing, disrupts sleep patterns and leaves us emotionally out of sorts, which can provide triggers for attacks.

One important line of research has focused on brain systems that control stress hormones such as cortisol. Cortisol and other stress hormones play an important role at times of emergency: they help our bodies make energy available to enable effective responses, temporarily suppress the immune system and sharpen attention. However, a number of studies conducted in people with depression indicate that excess cortisol released over a long time span may have many negative consequences for health. Excess cortisol may cause shrinking of a brain structure required for the formation of certain types of memory (hippocampus).

Panic and anxiety play havoc with blood sugar, which causes mood swings, tearfulness, fatigue and lack of concentration. What's more, it places pressure on the liver (which is responsible for releasing glucose) and the adrenal glands, as well as just about every other system in the body.

Headaches are caused not only by tension and fear, but also by the effects of adrenaline and by low blood sugar, all of which are associated with stress and, through that, panic attacks. Attacks rob the body of key B vitamins which help to keep the nervous system functioning well. Paradoxically, we are able to absorb far less of these B vitamins from food during attacks, because the digestive system effectively shuts down.

Diarrhoea, nausea and vomiting are all common side-effects of panic disorder, as digestion is disrupted through the stress response and fear. More serious, however, are chronic problems such as irritable bowel syndrome (IBS) and colitis, all of which are on the increase. IBS, for example, is a digestive disorder that causes abdominal pain, bloating, gas, diarrhoea and constipation – or a combination of these problems. IBS affects people of all ages, including children, and studies show that almost half of all cases of IBS are related to anxiety.

This relates back to immunity and to problems with nutrient absorption, both of which are related to the stress and fear associated with panic disorder. Allergies have increased dramatically, including those related to food (see page 33). Many food allergies have been linked to a deficiency of digestive enzymes, which could be a direct result of inadequate digestion caused by panic disorder. As food intolerance is believed to be a cause of panic disorders in some people, this is highly relevant.

When they are placed under constant pressure, the adrenal glands can become exhausted and fail to perform properly. This has numerous implications, the most serious of which is an inability to release the correct hormones in the correct amounts. Adrenal fatigue can affect sexuality, self-esteem, energy levels and the overall ability to cope. In the end we reach something known as 'burn-out', a feeling that many panic attack sufferers will recognise in the hours following an attack.

Panic and anxiety affect hormones in dramatic ways. According to Dr Marilyn Glenville, PhD, stress and fear have a direct effect on the reproductive system:

*'Women going through a bereavement or other kind of trauma, for instance, can stop having periods. Furthermore, the hormone prolactin can also be released when we are under stress and living under a cloud of fear, and this hormone is known to aggravate breast tenderness and may also be connected with depression.'*

Dr Glenville also points out that the adrenal glands are responsible for producing the sex hormones oestrogen and testosterone, in addition to those hormones produced by the ovaries. Not only can this affect the onset and regularity of periods, but it may also cause long-term fertility problems. If the adrenal glands are effectively 'worn out', they will not be able to produce the hormones necessary for ovulation. Later in life this can be even more dangerous, as the adrenal glands take over from the ovaries around the time of the menopause, producing oestrogen that can protect against osteoporosis.

During a panic attack the blood clots more quickly, greatly increasing the possibility of a stroke. Blood pressure is also raised (placing pressure on the heart, causing it to enlarge and weaken over time).

Like every other system in the body, the liver is under pressure in stressful conditions. The liver is the detoxifying organ of the body, responsible for clearing out the toxins with which we are in contact. These come in the form of environmental toxins (such as pollutants), food additives and preservatives, and every other harmful substance with which we come into contact. Although the liver has the ability to renew itself, it can, however, become less efficient and eventually fail. Stress associated with panic disorder, and the effects of recurrent attacks, cause the liver to produce glycogen to keep blood sugar levels steady. The high incidence of diabetes is, perhaps, one indication that liver exhaustion is occurring. The link between stress and liver problems cannot be ignored.

Many people become increasingly reliant on caffeine, alcohol, nicotine and drugs in order to mask their feelings of fear and anxiety, and to 'force' relaxation in an attempt to ward off an attack. All of these 'quick-fix' solutions are implicated in panic attacks, which means that this type of dependence can actually fuel the condition itself. The health risks of alcohol abuse, for example, are worrying enough. Not only does this put pressure on the liver, which is already working overtime dealing with the effects of stress, but long-term abuse of alcohol – even on a binge-drinking basis – can cause heart disease and damage to the brain, liver, pancreas, digestive system and central nervous system. Alcohol also causes metabolic damage to every cell in the body and depresses the immune system. It over-stimulates the adrenal glands, and the effect on blood sugar levels and brain chemistry is significant. The physical effects are dangerous enough, but alcohol also increases feelings of paranoia, feeling out of control, anxiety and depression.

## Are Panic Attacks Becoming More Common?

They do seem to be on the increase, although it's difficult to know whether this is because they are more clearly defined by the medical profession and people are less wary or embarrassed about reporting occurrences. There is also no doubt that stress plays a key role in laying the ground for panic attacks (see Chapter Two), and that stress is on the increase. In the UK, government figures and financial experts claim that stress is costing the economy a whopping £100 billion per year – with 40 percent of job turnover due to stress, 12.8 million working days lost in the UK, 58 percent of workers complaining of being over-stressed, causing lower productivity.

Most of us get inadequate exercise (which is necessary to reduce the effects of stress, caused by a build-up of adrenaline), eat poorly, fail to get enough sleep and have little real relaxation. Furthermore, we depend more heavily on alcohol for instant relaxation. This robs the body of the B vitamins required to ensure the health of our nervous system, and can lead to panic attacks in itself (see page 75). Relaxation tends to be achievement-driven rather than for enjoyment only (mastering a tennis shot, for example), or takes the form of distractions, such as television, which is ultimately stimulating. We rarely have times of peace and calm in order to reflect and attain an emotional stability. In Chapter Four we'll look at some positive ways to relax, but it's worth noting here that our collective inability to schedule time for rest and relaxation is a contributing factor to the modern plague of panic and anxiety.

In the context of a stressful lifestyle, it's not surprising that more and more of us are feeling anxious and under pressure. There are a number of other causes of panic attacks, discussed more fully in the next chapter, and many of these are the result of our 21st-century lifestyle.

## Do I Have a Panic Disorder?

The American Psychiatric Association has produced the following self-test. The best advice is to complete the test and show the results to your doctor. If you have suffered only one attack, and have experienced some of the symptoms in the first section, you do not suffer from panic disorder and steps can be taken to divert another attack (see Chapter Five).'Yes' answers in the second section denote a panic disorder.

For each question below, answer either Yes or No.

*Section One*
● Are you troubled by repeated, unexpected 'attacks' during which you are suddenly overcome by intense fear or discomfort, for no apparent reason?


● During an attack, do you experience any of these symptoms?
  - pounding heart
  - 'jelly' legs
  - sweating
  - dizziness
  - trembling or shaking
  - feelings of unreality or being detached from yourself
  - shortness of breath
  - fear of losing control, going crazy
  - choking
  - fear of dying
  - chest pain
  - numbness or tingling sensations
  - nausea or abdominal discomfort
  - chills or overheating.

- Do you experience a fear of places or situations where getting help or escape might be difficult, such as in a crowd or on a bridge?

- Are you troubled by being unable to travel without a companion?

*Section Two*
- For at least one month following an attack, have you:
    - felt persistent concern about having another one?
    - worried about having a heart attack or going 'crazy'?
    - changed your behaviour to accommodate the attack?

Having more than one illness at the same time can make it difficult to diagnose and treat them all successfully. Illnesses that sometimes complicate an anxiety disorder include depression and substance abuse. With this in mind, please take a minute to answer the following questions:

- Have you experienced changes in your sleeping or eating habits?

- More days than not, do you feel:
    - sad or depressed?
    - disinterested in life?
    - worthless or guilty?

- During the last year, has the use of alcohol or drugs:
    - resulted in your failure to fulfil responsibilities with work, school, or family?
    - placed you in a dangerous situation, such as driving a car while under the influence?
    - led to you being arrested?
    - continued despite causing problems for you and/or your loved ones?

REFERENCE:
*DIAGNOSTIC AND STATISTICAL MANUAL OF MENTAL DISORDERS* (4TH EDN; WASHINGTON, DC: AMERICAN PSYCHIATRIC ASSOCIATION, 1994)

## Could It Be Something Else?

Anxiety attacks can mimic or accompany nearly every acute disorder of the heart or lungs, including heart attacks and angina. An American study reported that 25 per cent of patients entering the emergency room with chest pain were actually suffering from panic attacks, which were diagnosed correctly by cardiologists in only 2 per cent of cases. It is often difficult to distinguish between a heart condition and a panic attack.

Asthma attacks and panic attacks have similar symptoms and can also coexist. In addition, anxiety-like symptoms that accompany panic attacks are seen in many other medical problems, including epilepsy, hypoglycaemia (low blood sugar), adrenal-gland tumours, and hyperthyroidism and hypothyroidism (over- and under-functioning of the thyroid gland; see page 24). Women can also experience intense panic attacks with hot flushes during the menopause (see page 30).

The good news is that as many as 90 per cent of those who seek treatment for panic disorders will resume normal lives, often in a matter of months.

In Chapter Two we'll take a look at what causes panic attacks.

# ChapterTwo

# Causes and Triggers

The cause of panic attacks is not clearly known, although theories abound. We do know that panic attacks can be hereditary, and we also know that blood sugar, abnormal brain function and even hormones have been implicated. The real answer is that there may be many factors that affect our tendency to suffer from panic attacks, and they may be unique to each individual. In other words, a combination of biological and environmental factors are at the root – in much the same way as in other diseases, such as heart disease or even weight problems.

There is some evidence that people who have a tendency to panic are more likely to be perfectionists, always self-critical, always certain that they are going to mess up. Because they lack confidence, they have trouble taking risks and letting go of control. They also tend to have ongoing fears about their mental and physical health, and about the long-term implications of having a health problem. Having said that, although a few experts say that panic disorder is more common in people who have experienced separation anxiety as children, many experts feel that panic disorder afflicts emotionally healthy people, and that people with panic disorder are no more likely than the average person to have suffered from emotional problems at the time the disorder began.

Let's take a closer look at what the experts say.

## Nervous Dysfunction

According to the National Anxiety Foundation, panic disorder was once called 'anxiety neurosis' and was believed to stem from deep-rooted psychological conflicts and subconscious upsetting impulses of a sexual nature. Today, however, panic disorder is not considered to be an emotional problem, but a physical illness that causes emotional symptoms. One theory is that there is an abnormality in the nervous system – primarily in the function of a tiny nerve centre in the brain stem (*locus ceruleus*) and its associated nerve pathways. Because the *locus ceruleus* is located in the part of the brain that controls heartbeat, breathing and other vital functions, this would help to explain the physical symptoms that accompany an attack.

## Genetics

Certainly the biological theory carries weight with some experts. Researchers have found that it is possible to identify children as young as 18 months who show anxious behaviours that increase the chances of developing later anxiety disorders. These children – who are high on what is called an 'anxious temperament' scale – show crying, clinging and avoidance in the face of new or unusual events. They are shy with strangers (more than the average) and are slow to relax in groups. Evidence shows that it is this type of child who is most likely to exhibit anxiety and panic disorder in later life. School phobia and other childhood anxiety disorders may be early forms of panic disorder. Children of parents with panic disorder are more likely to exhibit fear and withdrawal in unfamiliar situations.

Studies show the risk of developing panic disorder is 15- 17 per cent in the first-degree relatives (sisters, brothers, children) of panic disorder patients. The risk for development in identical twins is 24 to 31 per cent. This indicates that panic disorder may be genetically transmitted.

Researchers may have found the genetic mutation that is to blame for most panic attacks and other anxiety disorders. *New Scientist* magazine reported that the discovery was made by a team at the Centre for Medical and Molecular Biology in Barcelona. The scientists studied families with a history of problems such as panic disorders, agoraphobia and social phobia.

They found that 90 per cent of the affected family members carried a genetic abnormality. The same mutation – DUP25 – was also present in most other unrelated people that they tested, but it was rare in people who had no anxiety problems.

Some of these genes manufacture proteins that play a crucial role in controlling the way the cells of the nervous system communicate with each other. It may be that an imbalance in the production of these proteins makes the brain over-sensitive to stressful situations. However, the scientists stress that not everybody who carries the

DUP25 mutation is likely to suffer from anxiety disorders.

Researchers claim that, 'In the affected families 20 per cent of people with DUP25 had no anxiety illness at all.' The team is now trying to identify exactly which genes on DUP25 are linked to anxiety disorders. If they can do this, it might be possible to find drugs that suppress either the genes or their protein products. However, this could take several years.

Scientists have also discovered that the DUP25 mutation can change from generation to generation. It even varies within individuals – not all cells from some patients had the mutation.

Professor Roger Baker, an expert in panic disorders and a clinical psychologist based at Dorset Healthcare NHS Trust, has said that it is likely that panic attacks are caused by a mixture of genetic and environmental factors. He says that people who have a parent who has experienced panic disorder are up to seven times more likely to develop a similar disorder than other members of the population.

However, between a half and three-quarters of people who came for treatment had no parental history of the disorder.

Professor Baker has also found that approximately 8 per cent of panic attacks are caused by the misuse of drugs.

He says: 'It is not a simple matter, it is probably a balance of different factors. It may well be that some people have a general susceptibility to panic attacks, but they would probably need some sort of stressful event to set it off.'

Professor Baker also believes that a panic attack is essentially a normal response to fear triggered at an inappropriate moment. His research has shown that people who experience panic attacks tend to suppress their emotions. It might be that this tendency leads to emotions being bottled up until a panic attack is their only release.

Often the critical factor is not the panic attack itself, but the way the sufferer responds. Secondary factors such as misinterpreting the attack as a heart attack or impending madness, and avoiding situations that might trigger panic attacks, interfere with the person's life more than the actual panic attack itself.

## In Rare Cases ...

There would seem to be yet-to-be-identified factor which causes a rare, inherited form of panic disorder, in which the panic attacks may be extremely severe and resemble seizures closely enough to lead to misdiagnosis. Such attacks, although very rare, can be fatal. However, such panic attacks never show seizure-like brain activity in an EEG (electroencephalogram, which records the electrical impulses produced by the brain), although they can be seen in a PETscan (position emission tomograph, a type of three-dimensional scanning). Reports regularly occur of this form of panic disorder being misdiagnosed as temporal lobe epilepsy. One prominent expert on panic disorder has referred to a panic attack in this variant of panic disorder as 'conceptually a seizure that is not in the cortex of the brain', going on to state that the condition is 'closely related to anxiety, but is really a different disease'.

## Thyroid Disorder

One of the key symptoms of a serious thyroid condition is panic attacks. Research shows that screening has failed to pick up hypothyroid conditions (under-activity of the thyroid gland) which may be causing attacks in sufferers. In fact, even when thyroid disorder is finally pinpointed as the cause, and subsequently treated, some sufferers continue to experience attacks because of damage done to their nervous system, and because they have entered the cycle of fearing attacks that leads to panic disorder.

## Serotonin

There is also evidence to suggest that panic attacks can result from low levels of serotonin. Serotonin is one of a group of chemical messengers known as neurotransmitters which carry out communication in the brain and body. The message molecules flow from a nerve cell (neuron) on to other neurons which act as receivers. There, they attach to a distinctly shaped area on the neuron called a receptor site. This union, which is like a key fitting into a lock, triggers signals that either allow the message to be passed on to other cells or prevent the message from being forwarded. Since the discovery of serotonin in the 1950s, researchers are finding evidence that one of its roles is to mediate the emotions and judgement.

Some scientists believe that low activity of serotonin in the brain can lead to an underlying inability to handle powerful feelings, which can result in impulsive acts, aggressive behaviour, panic attacks and even suicidal tendencies. Serotonin is implicated in cases of depression and, because depression and anxiety often comprise the same syndrome, it's very likely that low serotonin is a contributory factor.

But are we born with low serotonin, or an inability to use it, or is it something that occurs as a result of environmental factors? This is something that is not clearly understood, but the serotonin theory does explain in part why some people are unable to control powerful emotions and panic, and why others are largely unaffected.

## The Behavioural Theory

Some experts believe that panic attacks are 'learned behaviour' – which means, in a nutshell, that we learn to become afraid of the possibility of having a panic attack, after even just a single attack, which may have been triggered by a life event or an illness. Obviously we do learn to fear something that has caused us a great fright, and the argument is that we therefore respond, both emotionally and physically, to something that we remember as being terrifying. And we do so with exactly the same symptoms. It is believed that these negative thought patterns feed the fear and create the attacks.

## Psychodynamics

This theory relates to childhood and its impact upon adult life. Experts believe that experiences in childhood – ranging from simply poor self-esteem to abuse – can cause panic attacks later in life. Many sufferers were abused as children, but an equal number were not, so it isn't simply abuse at the root here. It is thought that children who are parented in too authoritarian a manner (which led to a suppression of self-identity and an intrinsic belief that they were 'bad') or too lax a manner (if children are given no boundaries, they often struggle to form a strong self-identity) are more likely to suffer from anxiety and panic attacks.

There is no doubt that childhood feelings do affect adult behaviour and emotional health. Feelings of helplessness, powerlessness, worthlessness and that we are unworthy of love and affection are personal stresses that filter through from childhood to adult life. It's worth examining your own childhood to see if this could be at least partly the cause of your panic disorder.

Patients with panic disorder often describe their parents as over-protective, restricting, controlling, critical, frightening or rejecting.

## Childhood Separation Anxiety or Behavioural Inhibition

School phobia (see page 40) and other childhood anxiety disorders may be early forms of panic disorder. And, as mentioned earlier, children of parents with panic disorder are more likely to exhibit fear and withdrawal in unfamiliar situations.

*Sarah's Story*
Sarah had a normal middle-class upbringing and suffered from no major health problems throughout her childhood and adolescence. She was one of four children with authoritarian parents. She always suffered from self-esteem problems and the fear that she was not quite good enough. In her twenties, she wrote a novel that was met with great acclaim, and she found herself in the media spotlight. Before appearing on a radio programme, she experienced her first panic attack.

She suddenly felt all sense of normality disappear, and she shook uncontrollably for several minutes. Her mind went blank, her heart raced, her mouth was dry and she felt like she might faint. Worse still, Sarah felt like she might blurt out something inane, or actually run out of the room. She had no understanding of why this was happening, and was terrified by the episode.

Once she had regained her composure, Sarah was able to carry on with the interview, which was a success. It was, however, the beginning of a series of panic attacks that would plague her life. The first attack had occurred after a sleepless night, during a period of stress and after drinking several cups of coffee. These conditions were not completely unusual, however, so Sarah was at a loss to explain why she had experienced such a sense of panic.

Several months later, after experiencing repeated attacks in similar situations, Sarah realised that her own insecurity was the root of the problem. She felt that she was in some way undeserving of the attention she was receiving, and believed that she was unworthy of it. The radio programme had taken place at a time when her resources were low and her insecurities had overwhelmed her, causing her first attack.

Sarah underwent several counselling sessions and began to see how her childhood had affected her self-image. She was gradually able to build up her own self-esteem to the point that she could accept the attention she was receiving, and feel worthy of it. Her panic attacks were intermittent over the period of her counselling, and eventually disappeared completely.

## Stress

Stress has a profound effect on the nervous system and every other function of the body, and undoubtedly affects our emotional health on every level. Many of the symptoms of stress are exhibited in a much more extreme way during a panic attack. Several US studies claim that one in ten of us actually inherits a low stress tolerance or threshold, which means that 10 per cent of the population is already at a disadvantage. It's fairly obvious that some people thrive on high pressure, while others are less able to cope, and there is a genetic basis to this.

Consistent stress places enormous strain on the body, causing the following symptoms:

- over-eating and obesity
- loss of appetite and anorexia
- substance abuse
- irritability
- difficulty making decisions
- suppressed anger
- difficulty concentrating
- loss of sense of humour
- paranoia
- feeling out of control
- feeling unable to cope
- inability to finish one job before starting another
- tearfulness
- lack of interest in hobbies
- constant tiredness, even after sleep
- headaches
- chest pains

- palpitations
- indigestion
- nausea
- loss of appetite
- diarrhoea
- constipation
- flatulence
- stomach cramps
- tremors and shaking
- fainting
- nervous twitches and ticks
- foot-tapping
- nail-biting
- jumpiness
- insomnia and other sleep disorders (see cortisol)
- muscle cramps and spasms
- neck pain
- increased sweating
- menstrual irregularity
- frequent urination
- increased susceptibility to viruses
- frequent colds and flu
- itching
- worsening of chronic conditions, such as asthma and eczema.

It's easy to see from this list why panic attacks can be triggered, or even caused, by constant stress. When the body is under strain, nothing works effectively, and that includes our normal response to situations. What's more, because digestive function is affected, we do not absorb the nutrients we need from our food. Nutrients such as the B vitamins, which are crucial to the health of the nervous system, may be deficient, which would give rise to feelings of panic and even a full-blown attack itself.

Blood sugar and stress are also strongly related. When blood sugar drops, adrenaline – the stress hormone – kicks in, and with it come all the symptoms of stress. When blood sugar levels are stable there are no surges of adrenaline that bring on feelings of being out of control, emotional, irritable and everything else.

Stress may trigger a first panic attack, or it may lay down conditions for further attacks in someone who has experienced only an isolated incident. It's difficult to escape stress in our 24-hours-a-day, seven-days-a-week society. But there are ways to ease the burden, and it's crucial that anyone suffering from panic attacks undertakes them (see Chapter Six).

## Post Traumatic Stress Disorder

Post-traumatic stress disorder (PTSD) follows a severe or terrifying emotional experience. Events which may trigger PTSD include serious accidents, violent attacks, abuse and war. Often emergency staff suffer from PTSD as a result of dealing with trauma. They may experience extreme distress, including unexpected flashbacks to the event, nightmares, depression, detached feelings, trouble being close to members of their families, irritability and mood swings, and even feelings of violence.

Symptoms usually begin within three months of the trauma, but sometimes they start many years later. Sometimes they last for only a short period, but they may be long-lasting if no help is received. Often people with PTSD suffer from other related anxiety disorders.

## Trauma

A shock or trauma of any nature can cause a panic attack, and lead to further attacks. Emotional injury is essentially a normal response to an extreme event. It involves the creation of emotional memories, which arise through a long-lasting effect on structures deep within the brain. The more direct the exposure to the traumatic event, the higher the risk for emotional harm. Trauma can comprise anything that shocks us on a conscious or even unconscious level. The events of 11 September 2001, for example, caused deep-seated trauma to many people who were not even physically involved. Other traumas include car accidents, divorce, bereavement, injury, being witness or subject to violence, and much, much more.

All people react differently to trauma, and some of us appear to be more affected than others, for reasons that are not clearly understood. Reactions to trauma may appear immediately after the traumatic event or days and even weeks later. Loss of trust and fear of the event occurring again are a common response, as are flashbacks, nightmares, emotional numbing, avoidance of any reminders of the traumatic event, depression, substance abuse and anti-social behaviour. Also common are withdrawal and isolation, physical complaints, sleep disturbances and confusion. Many people experience a single panic attack or a series of panic attacks following trauma, as a natural response, which can lead to further attacks and a panic disorder.

## Hormone Issues

Women appear to be most affected by hormonal changes, in the case of pregnancy, pre-menstrually (although there is an argument that hormones are not at the root of PMS), post-natally, in puberty and during the menopause. Oestrogen in particular seems to have a dramatic effect on emotions, causing mood swings, irritability, anxiety and tension, all of which can induce feelings of panic in susceptible people, and particularly in those who have previously experienced an attack. Many women experience their first panic attack during times of hormonal flux.

Hormones, too, are affected by stress. In response to stress, the adrenal glands produce higher levels of adrenaline. The adrenal glands use progesterone as the 'raw material' for producing the adrenal hormones. If more adrenaline is produced, then more progesterone is needed. So excessive adrenaline production can create a hormone imbalance where oestrogen is dominant.

Deficiencies in progesterone, or more likely an imbalance between progesterone and oestrogen levels, are often implicated in panic disorders. Panic disorder often goes into remission during pregnancy, with the greatly elevated levels of progesterone experienced then. It is also not uncommon for women to experience post-natal panic attacks as their progesterone levels decline precipitously. Abnormal testosterone levels can play a role in panic disorder, as can excessive levels of insulin in the presence of normal blood sugar levels. It is also common to see abnormal levels of cortisol (a stress hormone) in people who suffer from regular panic attacks.

## Alcohol and Recreational Drugs

There is interesting evidence indicating that marijuana can cause panic attacks in susceptible people, and many sufferers experience their first attack after partaking. It seems that even one encounter may be enough to set off the condition, and it is suggested that 'highly strung' individuals avoid the use of this drug, and any other drugs that alter consciousness.

Alcohol is a different story, and it may have more to do with changes in blood sugar levels (see page 32), which set the stage for attacks in susceptible people. Alcohol increases feelings of paranoia, and affects the normal functioning of the nervous system. According to US research, the abuse of alcohol is very common in panic disorder. It may take the form of binge-drinking, in which case the panic disorder is probably not controlled or successfully hidden, and in fact the alcohol will be a factor in making the attacks more frequent.

Researchers claim, however, that many sufferers tend to drink regularly to cover up the symptoms (to self-medicate, in other words), but not to excess. In this case, the disorder may be successfully hidden from other family members. Sometimes the individual is not even aware of having the condition, having forgotten the initial panic attack or staved off an impending initial attack with alcohol. It has been suggested that the reason women are diagnosed with panic disorder more frequently than men is that men drink more to cover their anxiety.

Smoking is another potential environmental cause of panic attacks, and one that seems to be implicated in many cases where sufferers are young. A team from New York's Columbia University and New York State Psychiatric Institute found that smoking may increase the risk of some anxiety disorders for teens and young adults. They found that teenagers who smoke at least 20 cigarettes a day are at greater risk of developing agoraphobia, generalised anxiety disorder and panic disorder in young adulthood. In fact, smoking increased the possibility of suffering from a panic disorder and/or a panic attack 16-fold.

One hypothesis is that anxious people are more likely to start smoking because they think cigarettes will calm their nerves and help them in social situations. However, the researchers found that teenagers who had already developed anxiety problems were no more likely to become heavy smokers than those who did not suffer from anxiety. Another theory is that smoking may make people anxious because it damages their breathing. It may also be that one of the effects of nicotine is to generate anxiety.

We've already looked at the idea that stress can play havoc with digestion, causing nutrients to be inadequately absorbed. This may affect
the way the body works on every level. A poor diet can also cause
problems. First of all, a diet high in refined foods and sugars (white
bread and pasta, white sugar, biscuits, etc.) will cause serious problems with blood sugar, sending it soaring quickly and then just as
quickly causing it to plummet. When blood sugar is high, we experience an adrenaline-like buzz and can feel restless, agitated, nervous
and edgy. When it falls, we feel irritable, unsettled, possibly shaky and
emotional. Adrenaline is released when blood sugar falls suddenly,
which creates the symptoms of stress. It's easy to see how this type
of scenario can set the stage for panic attacks.

There is also some evidence that a deficiency of essential fatty
acids (EFAs) can affect the nervous system, leading to problems
with anxiety and panic. EFAs are found in foods such as nuts, seeds
and oily fish. These essential fats are a vital component of every
human cell, and the body needs them to balance hormones, insulate
nerve cells, keep the skin and arteries supple and to keep the body
warm.

Other nutrients linked to anxiety and panic attacks include selenium and magnesium. One study showed that a low intake of selenium (which is found in cereals, brazil nuts, fish, shellfish and meat)
produced a higher incidence of anxiety, depression and fatigue. Supplementation was associated with a general elevation of mood and a
decrease in anxiety.

Magnesium is known as 'nature's tranquilliser' and a deficiency is
associated with mood swings, tension and anxiety, all of which can
precede or are associated with a panic attack. Magnesium is found
naturally in leafy green vegetables, nuts and seeds, soya beans,
whole grains, oats and dark chocolate, and deficiency symptoms
include nervousness and anxiety, palpitations, irregular heartbeat
and a tendency to 'startle' too easily.

### Caffeine

A huge number of studies have shown that high caffeine consumption is associated with higher anxiety levels, and others show that
patients with anxiety disorders and panic syndrome have an abnor-

mal sensitivity to caffeine. Why is it so bad? Caffeine has a diuretic effect on the body and so depletes valuable stores of vitamins and minerals that are essential for a healthy hormone balance. Caffeine is a stimulant and causes a fast rise in blood sugar, followed by a quick drop. This contributes to the roller-coaster ride of blood sugar swings and the release of adrenaline, both of which cause the symptoms associated with stress as well as panic attacks. The 'edgy' feeling experienced after having caffeine (in coffee, tea, caffeinated drinks or chocolate) creates the perfect conditions for a panic attack, and in those who suffer regularly it can compound the problem.

## Food Allergies and Intolerance

Food allergies and intolerance, too, can create the conditions for panic attacks in susceptible people. For one thing, there is a well-recognised theory that depression and anxiety can be caused by eating a substance to which you are sensitive. These foods may cause a variety of physical symptoms but, according to Patrick Holford, author of *The Optimum Nutrition Bible*, they can also act as a mechanism for 'brain allergies'. He says that, while this phenomenon is not clearly understood, it is thought to apply to perhaps as many as one in four people with emotional health problems. While different people react to different foods, the most common food allergens are wheat gluten, other gluten-containing grains (oats, rye and barley), and dairy products.

Food allergies are increasingly common, and the Royal College of Physicians claim that up to 10 per cent of the population suffer. While there are a host of accompanying symptoms, including arthritis, chronic fatigue syndrome, skin problems, headaches, insomnia and diabetes, anxiety is also a common feature, as are mood swings and panic attacks. Most symptoms do not occur immediately after eating an offending food, but creep up over a period of about 24 hours. It's easy, therefore, to live for years without knowing that a particular food is problematic for you.

Symptoms are often difficult to pinpoint, largely because they can seem innocuous in the early stages. The time it takes for symptoms to appear can also make it harder to link a reaction with a specific food. Some of us become intolerant after a course of antibiotics, or being exposed to pesticides or other toxins. Symptoms may become worse during periods of stress, or after illness, which also clouds the issue.

Some of the most common symptoms include:

- anxiety
- asthma
- bloating
- chronic sniffling
- constipation
- coughing
- Crohn's disease
- diarrhoea
- eczema
- excess mucus
- facial puffiness
- fatigue
- flatulence
- headaches
- hives
- IBS
- indigestion
- insomnia
- itchy eyes
- itchy skin
- mood swings
- mouth ulcers
- muscular aches
- nausea
- skin rashes (around the mouth, particularly, although the whole body may be affected)
- sore throats
- water retention
- wheezing

The best way to test for intolerance is to look for any changes in your health, even if it has been a slow, progressive change. Do you suffer from headaches or excessive fatigue after meals? Do you get inexplicable skin rashes, particularly around the mouth? Do you feel worse or, alternatively, elated, almost high, after a particular type of food? Do you crave a particular type of food constantly? Do you have a constantly runny nose or sniffle? If so, chances are you are suffering from a food intolerance, and it may be partly responsible for your panic attacks.

## Craving the Worst Foods

This is an unusual feature of food intolerance, and it may be something that you have noticed in your own diet. There is plenty of evidence to suggest that we crave the foods to which we are intolerant. Some studies show that at least 50 per cent of us suffer food cravings for problem foods. We may even be unaware of it. Take a look at your own diet and see what foods you eat most commonly.

## Sleep

Even occasional sleeping problems can make daily life feel more stressful or cause you to be less productive. A survey in the US showed that people who get enough sleep report a better ability to concentrate, accomplish required tasks and handle minor irritations. In contrast, those with a higher 'sleep deficit' (regularly getting less than required) showed impairment of the ability to perform tasks involving memory, learning, logical reasoning and mathematical calculation. They also found relationships at home and at work more difficult.

It's worth noting that panic attacks and general anxiety can make sleep difficult, which does, of course, compound the problem. Similarly, in cases of severe depression people may wake early, or even in the middle of the night, and then be unable to get back to sleep. Furthermore, many sufferers experience panic attacks in their sleep, which cause them to waken with all the accompanying, frightening symptoms. An Australian survey found that 69 per cent of panic disorder sufferers experience a panic attack while going to sleep, and 86 per cent report that the panic attacks wake them from sleep at night. This creates something of a sleep phobia, in which we become afraid to sleep because of the possibility that another attack will arise.

## In Summary

While the number of theories about the cause of panic attacks can make it difficult to predict which applies to you, there is no doubt that making changes where you can, in terms of sleep, diet, stress and other elements of your lifestyle, will make a dramatic difference to the number of attacks you suffer, and your potential for suffering an attack at all. Genetic disposition can't be changed, but many other elements can. In ChapterThree, we'll look at how this can be done.

# ChapterThree

# The Problem with Panic: Phobias and Panic Disorder

A single panic attack can be an enormously disruptive and frightening experience, and many sufferers will feel bewildered and fearful for their health. It is this fear that drives a single attack into the repeated incidence that constitutes panic disorder. If more first-time sufferers understood that an isolated attack can be just that, and that there is no immediate threat of a recurrence, the number of victims of panic disorder would be reduced significantly. However, most of us are confused and deeply frightened by the experience, and these feelings lead to further attacks. And repeated attacks have the potential to harm our way of life in other ways, too.

Fear is a tangible experience and is preserved in the memory, often in stark clarity. What's more, many of us are embarrassed by the loss of control associated with a panic attack, and become concerned that we are in some way emotionally unstable or ill. We feel isolated, and as a result are perhaps unlikely to share our concerns with a doctor or a friend. Many sufferers go to great lengths to hide what they perceive to be a physical or even personality flaw.

While preparing this book and talking to victims of panic attacks, I was astonished to find that so many high-flying, successful people had shared similar experiences. Although many experts believe that it is often the tightly controlled perfectionist who is most likely to succumb at some point in their lives, it was interesting nevertheless to see this borne out by my research. But hiding such a dramatic experience, out of fear or a mistaken conviction that you are going mad or are in some other way unstable, has serious repercussions in many cases, and family and friends are often unable to help because they are simply unaware of the problem.

## Phobias and Panic Disorder

All people have fears, or situations they would rather avoid. Some people are frightened by job interviews. Others are uncomfortable on their own at night, or even during the day. Most people manage to control their fears, however, and continue with normal activities. Sometimes they develop coping strategies, such as turning on the television or radio to keep them company in an empty house, or spending long periods on the telephone to friends and family. Other times they merely grit their teeth and go forward.

But some people's lives are consumed by inappropriate and involuntary fears. Normal coping mechanisms don't work, and the need to avoid the objects or situations that cause anxiety can be so intense that normal living becomes impossible. These people are suffering from a phobia.

Individuals with phobias recognise that their fears are unreasonable, but they are unable to control them. Phobias are serious, real medical disorders. According to the National Institutes of Mental Health, they are thought to be caused by a combination of biological factors and life events, much in the way other disorders (such as diabetes or heart disease) are influenced by both a person's genes and his or her lifestyle.

Phobias are divided into three broad categories – specific phobia (which used to be called simple or single phobia), social phobia, and agoraphobia, depending on what triggers the fear and how the individual reacts to the dreaded object or situation. Agoraphobia – the word means 'fear of open spaces' – is one of the biggest problems associated with panic disorder. Social phobia is also common. In some cases phobias may pre-exist before panic disorder, with a panic attack occurring in a situation involving a phobia, but more often they are secondary, and the result of overwhelming fear.

## Specific Phobias

People with specific phobia suffer from an illogical but real and intense fear of certain things, such as dogs, insects, illness, blood, or a situation, such as flying, heights or exposure to deep water. Individuals experience extreme anxiety and panic when they are exposed to these objects or situations, even if they know, logically, that these things are not dangerous.

People can suffer from multiple specific phobias. Unlike social phobias or agoraphobia, specific phobias don't generally prohibit a person from living a normal life. Exposure and desensitisation can work wonders in terms of treating these specific phobias.

## Social Phobias

These involve a terror of a certain situation that might cause embarrassment. The trigger is normally having to 'perform', and is apparent in phobias about public speaking, using a public toilet, being watched while eating, or even fear of being touched. This fear elevates anxiety levels and produces a variety of symptoms which may include shaking, sweating, trembling voice, nausea, rapid heartbeat, hyperventilation, dizziness, blushing, tightness in the throat, 'mental blanks' and/or confusion. Anxiety becomes more intense when the person fears they're going to be singled out, ridiculed, criticised, embarrassed or belittled.

According to Carolyn Barker, co-ordinator of the Panic Anxiety Disorder Association in South Australia, 'Life is difficult for the person with a social phobia because they feel they don't fit in with everyone else. They feel something is wrong with them. Therefore, it is easier to stay away and avoid social contact whenever possible.'

*Fear of Public Speaking*
This type of fear is often the catalyst for a full-blown panic attack, and once experienced, the key to an extremely common phobia in modern life. According to US research, half of the population has nightmares about being on-stage in front of thousands of people and not knowing what they are supposed to do. The extreme embarrassment of having others stare at you – and, ultimately, judge you – represents the worst possible terror for many individuals.

It's worth knowing that a little stage fright is healthy – that adrenaline buzz invests a performance with energy and a critical edge. However, when many people experience that rush of adrenaline for the first time, they feel frightened and overwhelmed, leading to feelings of panic which can precipitate an attack. Over time, fear of further attacks causes a public-speaking phobia. In Chapter Four we'll look at specific remedies for phobias, including those associated with social situations, but it's worth noting here that this phobia is shared by a huge percentage of the population, and is usually curable.

Specific social phobia usually involves a phobic response to a specific event. For example, performance anxiety, or stage fright, is a specific social phobia that occurs when a person must perform in public. The incidence of social phobia is approximately 13 per cent and has been termed 'the neglected anxiety disorder' because it is often missed as a diagnosis.

A good example of a social phobia is school phobia in children. Many children hate to be the centre of attention, feel that they are being judged (in a negative fashion) by their peers, or are concerned about losing face or being embarrassed. These types of emotions can build up into a deep-seated fear of the whole experience.

As dramatic as it may sound, school phobia is quite common in children and adolescents, and there can be a variety of reasons for this condition. First of all, young children may have one negative experience at school, which they then build up in their minds into something traumatic. They then associate school with trauma, even if it is on a subconscious level, and no amount of rational discussion will sway them. Similarly, for children who lack confidence, find schoolwork difficult, or have problems with their peers, home is the safest place to be, and they are right to head towards safety.

Often a school phobia masks something else, and the negative emotions surrounding whatever is causing the upset can translate into headaches, abdominal pains, nausea and vomiting, and even fainting. Symptoms will necessarily be worse on weekday mornings, and better at weekends and during holidays. If, for example, there is any tension in the family, your child may feel that he needs to stay at home to prevent something terrible happening (a fight, a divorce, violence, or whatever he may have conjured up). If you are a parent and this scenario sounds familiar, consider whether there has been a traumatic event in your child's life, such as moving house, losing a loved one, or fighting with siblings, that may have triggered his or her phobia.

Never underestimate your child's concerns or fears. There may be a serious problem at school affecting his emotional health, or it may be something simple that has affected your child more dramatically than perhaps it should have done. Whether or not you consider a problem to be valid is irrelevant. If it is enough to cause your child to become upset, and to manifest physical symptoms, something has to be done about it.

*What to Do*

- The most important thing you can do is to get to the bottom of it. Spend as much time as you can with your child, talking things through. It may be that he is too traumatised or upset to talk about it, or he may be vaguely embarrassed or ashamed of his concerns. He may not even be able to pinpoint what the problem is – there may just be a general feeling of unhappiness and fear, or self-consciousness. Choose different times of the day for chats, and use personal examples to lead into discussions. For example, you can recount a childhood experience that upset you greatly. Children respond well to comparisons because it helps them believe that they are not weird or unusual.
- Talk to your child's teacher and, if necessary, other classmates, to find out what is wrong, and then work out a solution. Bullying may be one possibility and root cause of your child's fear of going to school.

## Can Children Suffer from Panic Attacks?

As many as 10 per cent of children and adolescents have some sort of mental disorder, according to the first ever UK government survey. The research, published by the Office of National Statistics, included emotional, behavioural and overactivity disorders, but it showed that 1 in 20 children in the UK has a 'clinically significant' disorder, with more boys than girls being identified. The survey involved face-to-face interviews with 10,500 parents of children aged 5 to 15, and 4,500 children aged 11 to 15. Emotional disorders include a wide range of problems such as over-anxiety, phobias, social phobias, panic attacks, obsessive – compulsive behaviour and depression. Behavioural disorders include awkward, troublesome, aggressive and antisocial behaviours.

*Preventing Panic Attacks in Children*

Most sufferers of panic attacks are concerned that they will somehow pass on the same problem to their children, and infect them with the same fears. Certainly over-parenting and over-cautious behaviour will have the effect of stimulating irrational fears in children, but it's unlikely that you will damage your child if she is raised in the context of a loving home environment.

Self-esteem is very much the key to ensuring that your child is able to cope with the rigours of life. She will need a physical and emotional outlet, on a daily basis, and be able to discuss and rationalise any fears or anxieties she feels. Even highly strung children are unlikely to succumb to panic and anxiety if they feel good about themselves, and understand that they have within them the tools to cope with upsetting experiences.

One of the keys to this is to avoid being an over-protective and authoritarian parent. Allow your child a little space to make decisions, to develop self-awareness, to make mistakes and to experiment a bit with life. Like adults, children need to have some control over their environment to feel secure, to learn to make decisions and choices, and to have the self-respect and self-esteem necessary to manage in the modern world. Childhood is a time of fun and experimentation, but it is also a 'training ground' for adulthood. Children need to be given the opportunity to make their own decisions, develop negotiating skills, plan their time and their activities, experience success and failure through experimentation and activities, and feel that they have some control over their environment. People who feel in control are far less likely to feel anxious, and are far *more* likely to develop coping skills to deal with panic when it arises.

Remember to react calmly to situations that you find frightening. Phobias and fears are passed on in a number of ways, but mostly through learning. If you always shriek when you see a spider, for example, you can't expect your children to have a rational reaction when they see one. Children undoubtedly learn from experience, and it's important that you do not pass on your own negative feelings.

Respect your child and give him choices. Allow him to have some control over his environment and his own behaviour.

Consider, too, the pressure your child might be under at school. In the UK and increasingly in other parts of the world, even very young children are subjected to rigorous and regular standardised testing. In one study, 58 percent of teachers had seen entire classes suffer massive anxiety or panic attacks caused by testing and exams. Children under this sort of pressure find it difficult to cope, and lack the emotional and physiological awareness necessary to understand what is happening to them. They experience the same physical and emotional symptoms as adults, and are understandably frightened by the experience which does, of course, compound the situation in many cases.

There is also increasing evidence that poor-quality family life is at the root of the growing number of panic and anxiety attacks in children. Parents are busy, financially stretched, and have fewer extended family members nearby to help. Children spend more and more time on computers and games consoles, or plonked in front of TVs. They should be developing emotionally through interaction and communication with parents and friends, which provides a dearth of comfort, reassurance and advice. What's more, many busy parent are failing to discipline adequately, allowing children to undertake unsuitable and even adult activities long before they are ready. This is the 'growing up too soon' syndrome that characterises much of modern society. This can have dramatic repercussions. Children feel secure and less fearful when they know where they stand, and when they understand their boundaries. When children lack boundaries, or they become elastic and ever-changing, their world becomes less defined and more frightening. Emotional health and freedom should always take place within the confines of a structured environment. Giving too much freedom can be alarming. That doesn't mean being authoritarian; it simply means offering suitable freedoms at appropriate times when a child is emotionally ready.

It's important to watch out for risky behaviours, which can be feeding anxiety and panic attacks. Just as caffeine, alcohol, tobacco and drugs can set the stage for panic attacks in adulthood, children can be affected by their use – and sometimes even more so, as their immature systems struggle to balance the effects.

One study found that children who suffer from regular panic attacks have a reduced ability to problem-solve. It is very important that parents offer opportunities for children to learn this essential skill, which has been shown in a variety of studies to aid emotional and cognitive development, as well as behaviour – all of which can underpin anxiety disorders. You can, for example, actively ask for their advice on household matters or problems that arise, from time management, to plotting a journey, organising the rota of household chores and even baking a cake. Your child needs to become used to being faced with tasks and coming up with plans and solutions when necessary. Make a big effort to encourage problem-solving by listening when your child has a problem, and helping your child to define it. Ask questions such as 'what would happen if you tried to . . .' or 'Let's think of three strategies, and see which one works best.'

Together, come up with some solutions and choose the best one. Afterwards, talk about what worked and what you could try next time. Always avoid leaping in with your own solutions, or offering to 'do it for you'. Children learn nothing unless they are given the opportunity to make choices and decisions.

Above all, be there for your child. A child who lacks the ability and opportunity to communicate with key role models, such as parents, will feel out of their depth, and more likely to suffer from anxiety and related disorders. Children simply do not have the tools, the insight, the experience or the confidence to face every problem on their own. Part of life is learning how to deal with different people and situations, and parents need to be involved along the way, to ensure that the little things don't become insurmountable issues.

Above all, give your child an outlet, and don't expect her to be angelic all the time. Everyone needs to let off steam. Children in particular need to be allowed to be children. Don't expect adult behaviour from a child. They do not have the self-control or the same sense of propriety, or even an understanding of societal expectations. As your child grows older she will learn, through you, and through the reactions of everyone else around her, what is appropriate. Until then, let your children be children. Delight in their boundless energy, their imagination, and the way they view the world. Don't stamp out that natural enthusiasm for life. Give it room to blossom within guidelines that your child understands and accepts.

## Agoraphobia

Panic disorder frequently occurs in combination with agoraphobia. People with agoraphobia are afraid of being in public places from which they think escape would be difficult. Paradoxically, some are frightened of being alone. Some agoraphobics stop using public transport, shopping or visiting places where there are likely to be other people. Others refuse to leave their homes, often for years at a time. Some will leave home only when accompanied by a trusted companion.

Some agoraphobics never have panic attacks, and many people with panic disorders do not develop agoraphobia. But large numbers suffer from both disorders. Their chief concern is about having a panic attack in public or in a place where they think help or safety is not immediately available. Worry about future panic attacks becomes a preoccupation for people with agoraphobia, and each new episode reinforces this fear.

Agoraphobia is a very complex phobia, usually manifesting itself as a collection of interlinked phobias. For example, many agoraphobics also fear being left alone (monophobia), dislike being in any situation where they feel trapped (exhibiting claustrophobia-type tendencies) and fear travelling away from their 'safe' place, usually their home. Some agoraphobics find they can travel more easily if they have a trusted friend or family member accompanying them; however, this can quickly lead to dependency on their carer. The severity of agoraphobia varies enormously between sufferers, from those who are housebound, even room-bound, to those who can travel specific distances within a pre-defined boundary.

About half of all people with panic disorder are afraid to leave home – often because they fear panicking and losing control away from their home environment. About 50 per cent of agoraphobia cases have been found to have been preceded by a panic attack. Forty-two per cent of adults with agoraphobia report having experienced separation anxiety from a parent (home) when they were children, suggesting a long personal history of this fear.

Panic attacks are more likely to occur initially during a stressful period involving a loss, such as after divorce or a death in the family, but many occur without any obvious precipitating stresses.

## Have You Got a Phobia?

Phobias are the most common kind of anxiety disorder. If you suspect that you may suffer from a phobia, complete the following self-test. Experts recommend that you show this to your doctor, who will be able to assess the situation properly. However, 'yes' answers are likely to indicate phobic tendencies, so it's worth seeking help if you answer 'yes' to more than two or three of the questions.

Are you troubled by:
● powerful and ongoing fear of social situations involving unfamiliar people?

- fear of places or situations where getting help or escape might be difficult, such as in a crowd or on a bridge?
- shortness of breath or a racing heart for no apparent reason?
- persistent and unreasonable fear of an object or situation, such as flying, heights, animals, blood, etc.?
- being unable to travel alone, without a companion?

## Generalised Anxiety Disorder

Panic attacks can precipitate, or be part of, a generalised anxiety disorder (known as GAD). This syndrome is much more exaggerated than the normal anxiety people experience day to day. It is chronic and overwhelming worry and tension, even though nothing seems to provoke it. Having this disorder means always anticipating disaster, often worrying excessively about health, money, family or work. Sometimes, though, the source of the worry is hard to pinpoint. Simply the thought of getting through the day provokes anxiety.

People with GAD can't seem to shake their concerns, even though they usually realise that their anxiety is more intense than the situation warrants. People with GAD also seem unable to relax. They often have trouble falling or staying asleep. Their worries are accompanied by physical symptoms, especially trembling, twitching, muscle tension, headaches, irritability, sweating or hot flushes. They may feel light-headed or out of breath. Nausea and a frequent need to urinate and/or diarrhoea are common features. Many sufferers complain of feeling like they have a lump in their throats. Depression is also common.

GAD is not normally a feature of agoraphobia, and most sufferers are able to live normal lives, going to work and socialising. However, it does undermine their quality of life and, when it becomes severe, it can be difficult for sufferers to carry out most daily activities.

GAD comes on gradually; it most often hits people in childhood or adolescence, but can also begin in adulthood. It's more common among women than men, and often occurs in relatives of affected persons. It's diagnosed when someone has spent at least six months worrying excessively about a number of everyday problems.

In general, the symptoms of GAD seem to diminish with age, and there are a wide range of treatments – most of which are successful – now available.

# Understanding Where Your Panic Disorder Began

The best way to ascertain where your panic attacks began is to jot down as many details as possible about the first occurrence:

- Were you under particular stress?
- Had you been ill?
- Did you experience a trauma of any kind (divorce, bereavement, injury, loss of job, etc.) in the six months prior to the attack?
- Where were you?
- Who were you with?
- What symptoms did you experience?
- How did you feel afterwards?
- Were you on any medication?
- Had you had too much to drink, or experimented with drugs in the 48 hours before the attack?

Try to remember as many details as you can about the experience, and the events leading up to it. You will probably find that there were extenuating circumstances that made you more susceptible. With that knowledge, it's easier to see why it happened, and this type of self-awareness is crucial to the recovery process. Chances are it would have been a one-off occurrence had you realised why your body reacted in such a way.

*Terry's Experience*
I have learned to circumvent panic attacks at night just by forcing myself to think about something else. Even if it means switching on the radio at 3 a.m. There is no point in worrying over things at that time in the morning! In general, you have to learn the difference between constructive worry that leads you to a solution, and non-constructive worry that just wastes time and energy. I just let the fear go and concentrate on other things. It's exhausting, sometimes, but I have managed to control them by sheer force of will.

## A Panic Diary
The next step towards recovery is to keep a panic diary. Chart each attack after it occurs. Note the circumstances under which it started (whom you were with, where you were, what you were doing, how you felt), and then note the physical symptoms that accompanied

the attack. Finally, make a note of what you did to get through it – did you talk yourself round, pace, or concentrate on your breath-ing? What passed through your mind? Give the attack a rating from one to ten in intensity. Keeping this record will show you your progress when you begin to use some of the various means of keeping control.

In the next chapter, we'll look at the ways of overcoming panic disorder, and some of the tried-and-tested means of intervention.

# Chapter Four

# Healing Yourself: Treatment Options

One of the keys to overcoming panic attacks is self-awareness. In Chapter Three we mentioned keeping a panic attack diary; this will help you to gauge the situations that instigate attacks, and give you crucial information about the triggers. Many people find that environmental factors (diet, alcohol, sleep and stress, for example) are implicated in their attacks, and it's not surprising. Everything that has an impact on your physical health will affect your emotional health, and if you are prone to panic attacks, you may be more sensitive than others to external stimuli. In Chapter Six we will look at the importance of a healthy lifestyle, which can have a dramatic effect on overall health and well-being. Here, however, we'll look at some of the help available for panic attack sufferers.

There's no harm in experimenting with a variety of different therapies and tools, but try them one at a time and record, in your panic diary, how successful they are. Above all, however, allow yourself some time to explore the feelings preceding and taking place during your attacks.

## The Conventional Approach

Many sufferers are offered help by their doctors, and this approach can be largely successful. However, because much of this type of intervention is palliative, or based on someone else taking charge, there is often an underlying fear that attacks will return when medication or therapy is stopped, for example. Many of these problems can be overcome by using some of the more natural approaches (see page 55), which often address the root of the problem and treat you as a whole (mind, body and spirit) rather than a series of malfunctioning parts.

For the purpose of this book we are using the 'generic' (drug group) names for medications mentioned, as these are the recognised international names for the drugs. These names may not be familiar to you, as you may see only the drug company's brand name on drugs prescribed for you. The generic name should appear on the packaging.

## Antidepressants
Antidepressant drugs are usually the drug of choice – in particular, paroxetine, imipramine or desipramine. In some cases a medication to relieve anxiety, such as lorazepam or alprazolam, may be given alone or with other medications. Also used is fluoxetine.

Most of the antidepressant drugs are known as Selective Serotonin Reuptake Inhibitors (SSRIs), and they work to ensure that serotonin (see page 24) is used properly by the brain. The most common side-effect, which tends to resolve over time, is mild nausea. Sexual dysfunction, primarily ejaculatory delay, also has been reported.

Antidepressants 'greatly improve' only about 30 per cent of patients with panic attacks and/or agoraphobia. The drug treatment approach is simple and takes six months to one year. However, there are several possible problems: some of these drugs are highly addictive (especially if one has a tendency towards alcoholism), and may have side-effects. It's worth noting that drugs do not solve underlying problems, if there are any.

### SSRIs
Fluoxetine, Citalopram, Fluvoxamine, Paroxetine, Sertraline.

### SNRIs (Selective Norepinephrine Reuptake Inhibitors).
This new class of drug, which is unrelated to other antidepressants, is used in the management of depression and anxiety.

## Benzodiazepines
The drugs used to reduce anxiety tend to be high-potency benzodiazepine tranquillisers. Some examples are nitrazepam, lorazepam and clonazepam. These medicines are quite effective, and normally have few side-effects at proper doses. They block panic attacks almost immediately, in the first day or two of treatment. There is some evidence that they are highly addictive, and therefore it is now suggested that they are used for no longer than 2 to 4 weeks, even in the most serious cases. Ironically, too, one of the side-effects of withdrawing from benzodiazepines is anxiety, rendering it largely useless as a long-term solution.

Alprazolam, Clobazam, Diazepam, Flurazepam, Lorazepam, and others less commonly used such as, Bromazepam, Oxazepam, Temazepam.

## Beta Blockers

Beta blockers are used mainly to reduce certain anxiety symptoms such as palpitations, sweating and tremors, and to control anxiety in public situations. They often are prescribed for individuals with social phobia, and for panic attacks. Beta blockers reduce blood pressure and slow the heartbeat.

- Propranolol
- Oxprenolol

## Tricyclics

Tricyclics use is not as widely recommended as it once was, particularly in view of several studies indicating that cognitive behavioural therapy was more effective than tricyclics in treating anxiety and panic attacks. In cases that don t respond well to other therapies tricyclics may be suggested however, these are currently used only rarely.

- Amitriptyline
- Amoxapine
- Clomipramine
- Desipramine
- Dothiepin
- Doxepin
- Imipramine
- Maprotiline
- Mianserin
- Nortriptyline
- Protriptyline
- Trazodone
- Trimipramine
- Viloxadine

## Monoamine Oxidase Inhibitors

Monoamine Oxidase Inhibitors (MAOIs) are drugs are used in the treatment of panic disorder, social phobia, and some other phobias. They are not always used, largely because they require dietary restrictions and some doctors prefer to try other treatments first. Anyone taking an MAOI must avoid other medications, wine and beer, and food such as cheeses that contain tyramine.

- Phenelzine
- Tranylcypromine

Medication is most effective when combined with psychological therapies. The chance of recurrence is reduced when medication and psychological therapies are used together.

## Behaviour Therapy

Behaviour (also called behavioural) therapy is a structured therapy originally derived from learning theory, which seeks to solve problems and relieve symptoms by changing behaviour and the environmental factors which control behaviour. Graded exposure to feared situations is one of the commonest behavioural treatment methods and is used in a range of anxiety disorders.

## Cognitive Behavioural Therapy (CBT)

CBT works on the principle that the thoughts that produce and maintain anxiety can be recognised objectively and altered using various techniques, thereby changing the behavioural response and eliminating the anxiety reaction. The goal is to regain control of reactions to stress and stimuli, thus reducing the feeling of helplessness that often accompanies anxiety disorders. A small study comparing cognitive therapy with emotional support therapy reported that, after two months, 70 per cent of those using cognitive therapy, but only 25 per cent of the other group, were free of panic attacks. Treatments are equally effective in men and women.

Treatment usually takes about 12 to 20 weeks. First, the patient must learn how to recognise anxious reactions and thoughts as they occur. These entrenched and automatic reactions and thoughts must be challenged and understood. One of the most important steps is to keep a daily diary that reports the occurrences of the anxiety attack and any thoughts and events associated with it. As the patient begins perceiving that false assumptions underlie the anxiety, he or she can begin substituting new ways of coping with the feared objects and situations. The essential goal of cognitive therapy is to understand the realities of an anxiety-provoking situation and to respond with new actions based on reasonable expectations.

As part of many of the CBT approaches, patients are taught techniques to reduce the physical effects of anxiety. For example, many people with anxiety disorders experience hyperventilation – rapid, tense breathing that expels too much carbon dioxide, resulting in chest pain, dizziness, tingling of the mouth and fingers, muscle cramps, and even fainting. Hyperventilation is one of the primary physical manifestations of panic disorders. By practising measured, controlled breathing at the onset of a panic attack, patients may be able to prevent full attacks. Relaxation methods, such as learning how to relax all the muscles gradually, may also be helpful.

Follow-up studies of Cognitive Behavioural Therapy indicate that short-term treatment can have lasting beneficial effects. In controlled trials, panic-free rates in excess of 80 per cent have been reported at follow-up periods of one to two years.

## Systematic Desensitisation

Systematic desensitisation is a specific technique that breaks the link between the anxiety-provoking stimulus and the anxiety response; this treatment requires the patient to confront, gradually, the object of fear. There are three main elements to the process: relaxation training, a list composed by the patient that prioritises anxiety-inducing situations by degree of fear, and the desensitisation procedure itself – confronting each item on the list, starting with the least stressful.

This treatment is especially effective for simple phobias, social phobias, agoraphobia, and post-traumatic stress disorder, although it is used by some therapists for the treatment of panic attacks.

The problem with this approach is, of course, the fact that it is not really a situation or place that causes the attack. The rationale behind graded exposure programs is that when the individual goes into situations and/or places he or she would normally avoid, and stays in that situation or place, the anxiety and/or panic attack will peak and slowly ebb away. In other words, the person will habituate (get used) to the anxiety and panic attack in that situation or place. As many sufferers point out, however, if they are not directly frightened of that situation or place itself, why would the anxiety 'ebb away' when it has never done so before?

## Exposure and Response Treatment

Exposure treatment purposefully generates anxiety, unlike the desensitisation process, which emphasises a relaxed approach and allows the patient to confront the sources of anxiety gradually. By repeatedly exposing the patient to the feared object or situation, either literally or using imagination/visualisation techniques, the patient experiences the anxiety over and over until the stimulating event loses its impact.

Two variants of exposure treatments are 'flooding' and 'graduated exposure'. Flooding, which exposes the person to the anxiety-producing stimulus for as long as one or two hours, has been helpful for some patients with most types of anxiety disorders. Graduated exposure, which can also be successful, gives the patient a greater degree of control over the length and frequency of exposure. Both types of exposure treatment use the most fearful stimulus first, unlike systematic desensitisation, which begins with the least fearful.

One study reported that prolonged exposure therapy for motor-vehicle accident survivors with acute stress disorder was effective in preventing full-blown PTSD (see page 29), which is extremely difficult to treat. Combining exposure with cognitive therapy (see page 52) may be particularly beneficial.

## Modelling Treatment
Phobias can often be treated successfully with modelling treatment: the sufferer observes an actor approach an anxiety-producing object or engage in a fear-provoking activity that is similar to the patient's specific problem. The goal is to learn how to behave in comparable circumstances. Either a live or videotaped situation may be used, although the live model is considered to be more effective. Virtual reality is also used, using computer-generated images to simulate a natural environment and allow interaction with it. Once again, this type of therapy, although used for panic disorder, might not be as useful as others, as the fear is not of a certain trigger situation or place, but fear of the attack itself.

## Psychotherapies
Other forms of psychotherapy, commonly called 'talk' therapies, deal more with childhood roots of anxiety and usually, although not always, require longer treatment times. They include interpersonal therapy, supportive psychotherapy, attention intervention, and psychoanalysis. All work is done during the sessions. Some experts believe that such therapies might be more useful for generalised anxiety, which may require more sustained work to process and recover from early traumas and fears.

## Hypnotherapy

Hypnotherapy is often the first port of call for people suffering from panic attacks, often in the mistaken belief that their attacks can be halted simply through the power of the mind. While, in theory, hypnotherapy is enormously relaxing, which will be beneficial, it is not a quick-fix solution to panic attacks. It does not teach people to take control of their thoughts, which is what needs to happen in an attack scenario. The best results for hypnosis appear to take place in conjunction with cognitive therapy.

## The Natural Approach

### Acupuncture

Acupuncture works by balancing the body's energy, to encourage it to heal itself. It can be used to treat a wide range of conditions, including disorders where conventional medicine has not been able to cure or even to find a cause for the condition.

Acupuncture is a medical technique practised in Traditional Chinese Medicine (TCM) which consists of inserting hair-thin needles into the skin at certain specific points called 'acupuncture points' or 'acupoints'. It has been used for more than 4,000 years, and is used not only for relieving pain, but for curing disease and improving overall health.

Chinese medical practitioners believe that a vital force, called 'chi', flows through our body in channels, or meridians. When this vital force, or energy, becomes blocked or stagnant, disease and dis-harmony result. Acupuncture works by stimulating or relaxing points along the meridians to unblock energy and to encourage its flow.

Twelve major meridians are identified in acupuncture, although practising acupuncturists make use of 59 major and minor meridians and up to 1,000 acupuncture points along the channels.

The first consultation will last for up to 90 minutes, and your therapist will take great trouble to make an accurate diagnosis, since the success of the treatment depends upon it. He or she will ask you questions about your health, lifestyle, medical history, symptoms, sleep patterns, sensations of hot and cold, any dizziness, eating habits, bowel movements, emotional problems, relationships, and many other factors. The therapist will also note various elements of your appearance, and take pulse readings on each wrist. There are six basic Chinese pulses, three on each wrist.

The therapist will then decide on a course of treatment to restore your energy, and ensure that you experience optimum health. The needles will be inserted into the skin, and then manipulated to calm or stimulate a specific point. He or she will use up to eight needles, which may be left in for about 30 minutes, or removed very quickly. Your acupuncturist may also suggest some Chinese herbal treatment, or dietary or lifestyle changes to go alongside treatment.

The needles are typically inserted $1/10$ to $4/10$ of an inch (0.3 to 1 centimetre) deep, but some procedures require the needles to be inserted as deep as 10 inches (25 centimetres). The acupuncture points are then stimulated, either by gentle twirling, by heat, or by stimulation with a weak electrical current. Acupuncture points can also be stimulated by pressure, ultrasound, and certain wavelengths of light. Occasionally herbs are burnt at acupuncture points – this technique is called moxibustion.

Acupuncture does not hurt, but you will feel a tingling sensation when the needle enters, and a little discomfort if the correct acupuncture points are addressed. It feels like a mild electrical shock running up the appropriate channel. After treatment you may feel quite profoundly different – either elated or perhaps exhausted.

The World Health Organization recognises the use of acupuncture in the treatment of a wide range of medical problems, including anxiety, depression, nervousness, stress reduction, and relaxation.

Acupuncture can be valuable in the treatment of panic attacks, mainly because it restores the body's equilibrium – on both a physical and an emotional level. Because so many features of panic disorder seem related to environmental factors, including stress, acupuncture can help to reduce the tendency for attacks to occur.

From a conventional point of view, acupuncture is known to release chemicals called beta endorphins, which are natural opiates in the brain that alleviate pain and encourage a sense of well-being. For this reason alone, it's worth a try.

*Kate's Experience*

I suffered from panic attacks for several years – although I can hardly remember the first one. I do remember fearing loads of different situations because they tended to happen when I was under pressure, and waiting in queues, for example, or before a social outing. I would find myself tongue-tied, blank, feeling like I might faint, sheet white and suffering horrendous palpitations. I also shook like a leaf, which was incredibly embarrassing.

I'm not sure I've completely mastered the attacks. They do come back from time to time (when I'm hungover, for example, or quite stressed), but I have tried a number of different alternative therapies to help me to remain calm, and they seem to have been working. My last attack was a year ago, so there is real progress. I have regular acupuncture sessions (which leave me enormously relaxed, and had the added and unexpected benefit of encouraging a fairly substantial weight loss); I see a homeopath, who has helped me to make progress in all parts of my life (I feel much more socially confident now, for example, and my overall health is better than it has ever been); and I use aromatherapy oils in the bath on a regular basis.

My greatest find, however, is Rescue Remedy, which I carry absolutely everywhere. If I feel panic start to creep on, I take a couple of drops and breathe slowly. It works extremely well, and has done now for a good 18 months. I feel confident now that I can live my life without fear or the fear of fear.

## Aromatherapy

Aromatherapy involves the use of essential oils, which are the 'life force' of aromatic flowers, herbs, plants, trees or spices, for therapeutic purposes. The word 'aromatherapy' literally means 'treatment using scents', and the therapy has evolved as a branch of herbal medicine. Unlike the herbs used in herbal medicine, essential oils are not taken internally, but are inhaled or applied to the skin. Each oil has its own natural fragrance and therapeutic action; some oils have many. Treatment involves applying these oils to the body to improve physical, mental and emotional health.

Essential oils enter the body by inhalation and by absorption through the pores of the skin. Once in the body they work in three ways: pharmacologically, physiologically, and psychologically. The chemical constituents of the oils are carried in the bloodstream to all areas of the body, where they react with body chemistry. Certain oils also have an affinity with particular areas of the body and their properties have different effects on body systems: balancing, sedating, stimulating, etc. When inhaled, aromatic signals are sent to the limbic system of the brain where they exert a direct effect on the mind and emotions.

57

There are many ways to use essential oils at home. In a massage o in the bath tend to be the most popular; these methods are also usually more effective than inhalation. However, there several othe techniques which are particularly beneficial for certain conditions These include steam inhalations, creams, lotions and shampoos gargles and mouthwashes, neat applications (only appropriate fo some oils), douches, and compresses.

Aromatherapy is gentle enough to be used by people of all age and states of health. It has been shown to be particularly effective ir preventing and treating stress and anxiety-related disorders, insom nia and depression.

Aromatherapy is compatible with conventional medicine and mos other forms of holistic treatment. However, if you are taking medica tion, consult your doctor. Some oils are not compatible with homeo pathic treatment (see page 70).

In terms of panic attacks, the stress-relieving properties of essentia oils, often in conjunction with massage, will be enormously benefi cial. Many oils have specific properties that help to ease anxiety and some can be used in the throes of an attack to ease symptoms – and even, in some cases, ward it off.

Some of the best oils are as follows:
● Bergamot, geranium and ylang ylang are used in the treatment o depression and anxiety.
● Roman chamomile, neroli and patchouli are calming.
● In periods of great stress, or following an attack, when you fee tired and without energy, try orange or peppermint.

A huge number of oils are sedative, and you may need to experimen a little to find the oil that suits you best. Many therapists believe tha we are instinctively drawn to the oil that best suits our present state, so don't hesitate to try out a few before you buy. The best sedative oils are: bergamot, chamomile, cedarwood, frankincense, geranium, jas mine, juniper, lavender, marjoram, melissa, patchouli, rose, sandal wood, verbena and ylang ylang.

## Autogenic Training
Autogenic means 'self-generation', because the suggestions for calm ing down and experiencing relaxation come from within. The idea is

that we can experience the same complete relaxation of hypnosis in the waking mind. In order to do this, you repeat to yourself, over and over, the phrases that convey a feeling that your body is comfortable and relaxed. Over time, your suggestion (much like an affirmation) takes over.

When we are truly relaxed, the arteries in the extremities open, increasing blood supply and imbuing us with a sense of warmth and pleasurable heaviness. We can normally remember this sensation, and can adjust our nervous system to recapture the memory of warmth and heaviness when we are in the midst of a panic attack.

In this state of deep relaxation, we are able to deal efficiently with stress, tension, emotional difficulties and panic.

A practitioner will teach you six basic exercises, which affect breathing and body function: relaxation of the neuromuscular system (relating to the nerves and muscles), relaxation of the circulatory system, regulation of the heart rate, adjustment of consciousness of breathing, creation of warmth in the abdomen, and coolness in the forehead.

There is documented evidence that physical changes do occur in the body as a result of these exercises, and it is felt that through this state of near-hypnosis you are effectively 'talking' your body and mind back to a state of well-being and relaxation.

Autogenic training can also be practised at home: scan your body from head to toe. Breathe from your abdomen (see page 65) and focus on each area of tension. As you exhale, visualise the area becoming warm and heavy. Practise this frequently so that you become accustomed to the sensation, and can remember it and therefore bring it on when required.

The best element of autogenic training is that it requires you to believe that you can heal yourself by reaching a relaxed physical and mental state that frees your body from unnecessary strains and stresses. All research points to the fact that in order to overcome panic attacks, we must take charge of our own thought process – and this therapy does appear to help us to do just that.

**Bach Flower Remedies**
This delightful therapy is misleadingly simple, but the results can be dramatic. Flower essences, or flower remedies, as they are more commonly known, are used therapeutically to harmonise the body,

mind and the spirit. The bottled flower essences are said to contain vibrations of the sun's energy, absorbed by the flowers' petals when they are immersed in sun-warmed water. The remedies use the vibrational essence of the flowers to balance the negative emotions which lead to, and are symptoms of, disease. They are a simple, natural method of establishing personal equilibrium and harmony.

Flower remedies do not work in any biochemical way, and because no physical part of the plant remains in the remedy, its properties and actions cannot be detected or analysed as if it were a drug or herbal preparation. Therapists believe the remedies contain the energy or 'memory' of the plant from which it was made, and work in a way that is similar to homeopathic remedies – on a vibrational basis .

Some of the remedies are known as 'type remedies'. Your type remedy is effectively the remedy that is most compatible with your personality or basic character, and it can be taken when the negative side of this character threatens the positive. The difficulty with the type remedy lies in analysing your character and deciding which remedy matches it best. For example, if you are a perfectionist and work hard to achieve results, this would be a positive side of your character. However, if you become obsessive about this work, aggressive and difficult to please, and demand too much of other people, then the negative side of this characteristic has taken over, and the appropriate essence would right the balance.

Flower remedies are ideal for home use, being simple to make and use. They are made in water, preserved with alcohol, and employ the ability of flowers to change and enhance mood, and to balance the negative emotions which contribute to ill-health.

Negative emotions depress the mind and immune system, repress activity and contribute to ill-health. Some of the most common negative emotions include: fear, uncertainty, loneliness, over-sensitivity to influences and ideas, despondency, over-concern for the welfare of others, and despair. Just before physical symptoms set in, you may notice tearfulness, irrational fears (of being alone, for example), depression or anxiety. These are all negative emotional states that can be addressed using flower essences.

Flower essences work to right negative emotions, improving well-being on an emotional level that transmits to good physical health. They can be used to prevent and treat illness by working on an emotional level.

Flower remedies can complement other types of therapies such as herbalism, homeopathy or aromatherapy, or they can be used alone. These simple and effective remedies can be used to:

- support in times of crisis
- treat the emotional symptoms produced by illness
- address a particular reoccurring emotional or behavioural pattern
- help prevent illness by identifying negative emotional states that are the precursors to ill-health.

Remedies act quickly; there should be an improvement within days, although it make take months to address fully a long-standing pattern.

In the context of panic attacks, flower essences can be extremely helpful, mainly because panic is based on fear, one of the essential negative emotions. There are 38 Bach Flower Remedies to choose from, and it makes sense to put together a blend that best suits your own personal state of mind. Choose from the following:

| | |
|---|---|
| Agrimony | For those who hide their feelings behind humour and put on a brave face |
| Aspen | For fear of the unknown; for vague, unsettling fears which cannot be explained |
| Beech | For the perfectionist who tends to be intolerant of other people's methods and experience |
| Centaury | For those who find it impossible to say no to others' demands, and thus exhaust themselves by doing too much |
| Cerato | For those who lack confidence in themselves and are constantly seeking the advice of others |
| Cherry Plum | For the fear of losing your mind and having irrational thoughts or demonstrating irrational behaviour |
| Chestnut Bud | For those who find it hard to learn from life and keep making the same mistakes |
| Chicory | For the self-obsessed, mothering type who is overprotective and possessive |
| Clematis | For the absent-minded day-dreamer who needs to be awake and have the mind focused on the here and now |
| Crab Apple | For those who feel unclean or polluted on |

any level – physical, emotional or spiritual;
for those who need a purification ritual

Elm
For those who suffer temporary feelings of
inadequacy brought on by their high
expectations of themselves

Gentian
For despondency and those who are easily
discouraged and set back in life; for pessimism

Gorse
For those who suffer hopelessness and despair
after a long struggle and who are stuck in a
negative pattern

Heather
For those who like to be the centre of things and
talk constantly about themselves; for poor
listeners

Holly
For those who develop the victim mentality and
suffer bouts of anger, jealously and envy

Honeysuckle
For those who suffer from nostalgia or who
dwell in the past to escape a painful future

Hornbeam
For those who are stuck in a rut and exhausted,
so that work which used to be fulfilling is now
tiresome

Impatiens
For impatience and irritability; for those who
are always in a rush and are too busy to slow down

Larch
For those who feel worthless and who are
suffering from lack of confidence or low
self-esteem

Mimulus
For the fear of known things; for the strength to
face everyday fears and all fears which can
be name, for example the fear of flying

Mustard
For depression and those who feel they are under
a dark gloomy cloud, for no apparent reason

Oak
For the fighter who never gives in and is
exhausting themselves by being too
narrow-minded in engaging in the same old fight

Olive
For those who are exhausted on all levels, fatigued
and drained of further optimism and spirit

Pine
For those who suffer self-reproach and guilt; for
those who say sorry even when things are not
their fault

Red Chestnut
For those who are overanxious for the welfare of

| | |
|---|---|
| | family or friends |
| Rock Rose | For those who feel helpless and experience terror or panic – there may or may not be a reason for this, but the feeling is real |
| Rock Water | For perfectionists who are hard on themselves and demand perfection in all things |
| Scleranthus | For those who suffer from indecision and who cannot make up their minds |
| Star of Bethlehem | For shocks of all kinds accidents, bad news, sudden startling noise and trauma |
| Sweet Chestnut | For utter despair and hopelessness, for when there seems no way out |
| Vervain | For over-straining and stress; for the perfectionist, hard on themselves and over-strained by trying to meet their own exacting ideals |
| Vine | For the over-strong and dominating leader who may tend towards tyranny; for bullying |
| Walnut | For change, breaking links so that life may develop in another direction |
| Water Violet | For people who are aloof, self-reliant and self-contained, to enable them to relax their reserve and become capable of sharing |
| White Chestnut | For tiresome mental chatter and the overactive mind, full of persistent and unwanted patterns of thought |
| Wild Oat | For those who need help deciding on the path and purpose of their lives |
| Wild Rose | For those who drift through life, resigned to accept any eventuality; for fatalists |
| Willow | For those who feel they have been treated unfairly; for pessimism and self-pity |

The most essential of the Bach Flower Remedies is Rescue Remedy (also called Five-Flower Essence), which is made from equal amounts of the five following essences:

● Cherry Plum – for feelings of desperation
● Clematis – to counteract the tendency to drift away from the present

- Impatiens – to soothe irritability and tension
- Rock Rose – to ease terror, fear or panic
- Star of Bethlehem – to address the mental and physical symp toms of shock.

At the first sign of a panic attack, take a few drops orally, or rub them into your pulse points. Many sufferers swear by this treatment, and gain enormous benefit.

The other key remedy is mimulus, for fear of known things. Because fear of another attack is the driving force behind panic dis order, this remedy is invaluable. It's also great for phobias such as fear of public speaking, or even school phobias in children, which are a 'known quantity'.

## Biofeedback

Biofeedback is a form of technologically supported relaxation ther apy which was developed in the US. Patients are taught a series of relaxation exercises similar to those of autogenic training (see page 59), but in biofeedback this is taken one step further and a patient's progress is monitored by machines which assess changes in heart rate, body temperature, muscle tension, skin conductivity and brain waves.

Once training is complete, patients learn how to recognise their body's signals and to reach a state of relaxation themselves, which is the basis of the therapy. Biofeedback trains patients to recognise the symptoms of stress, panic attacks, anxiety or anything else from which they suffer, and then to take the appropriate steps to deal with them.

The most common conditions which benefit from biofeedback are stress and anxiety-related disorders such as insomnia, digestive trou bles, headaches and high blood pressure, all of which are closely related to panic attacks, either as symptoms or as precursors.

## Breathing

There are several elements behind the idea that breathing can help to prevent and ease panic attacks. The first is that correct breathing can induce a feeling of relaxation so that the panic cannot take hold. The second is based on the premise that carbon dioxide may be at the root of the disorder in some people. Because we tend to hyperventilate when we feel panicky, or prior to and during an attack, we have an unequal balance of carbon dioxide to oxygen in our bloodstream, which can exacerbate symptoms and bring on feelings of panic.

Simple breathing exercises are easy to learn, and can be invaluable to anyone suffering from panic attacks. The first thing to do, however, is to learn to breathe from your stomach, not your chest, which ensures that you get full breaths, which affords better oxygenation to all of the tissues (including the brain) and removes excess carbon dioxide.

Lie on your back and place one hand on your chest. Keep it as still as possible. Place your other hand on your abdomen, just below your waistband. Press down gently, to force the air from this area. When you remove the pressure, it will bounce back. Try to breathe rhythmically and evenly from your abdomen, consciously trying to keep air out of your chest.

Now try this in front of a mirror, watching the action of your abdomen as it moves in and out. When you become comfortable, try this sitting upright on a hard-backed chair, and sitting on the floor. You may become light-headed at first, but with practice it will become easier.

This type of relaxed breathing is useful if any stressful situation. By calming your breath you will lower your blood pressure and heart rate, and trigger the relaxation response of the parasympathetic nervous system, which is essential in the case of anxiety and panic.

It's important, however, to learn to breathe properly all of the time, not simply in the throes of an attack. If you can concentrate on breathing correctly, through regular daily practice, you will be much more likely to ward off an attack, or certainly to experience fewer symptoms.

## ColourTherapy

Albert Einstein spent his whole life involved with the idea that everything in the universe is formed from vibrating energy, consisting of light, sound, and electricity. He developed the idea that all matter is made of atoms and molecules which vibrate in certain sympathetic patterns, and that it is the rate of vibration which holds them together, giving matter form and shape.

Energy is not confined to the physical world, for our thoughts and feelings also create energy patterns and vibrations. Vibrations pass freely between our emotional, mental and spiritual bodies, and so

the type of energy found in one of these areas will automaticall
affect the state of the others.

Research has begun to validate the importance of colour in th
treatment of disease. For example contemplating blue light ha
been shown to lower blood pressure, by calming the autonomic nei
vous system, while red light causes it to rise. Colour therapists clair
that every subtle change in colour affects us on every level of ou
being. It is a claim corroborated by published information b
research physicists, who state that the cells of the body are made u
of contracted light. By definition, cells made of light will respond t
colour.

The colours your choose for your environment will obviously hav
an effect on your mood, health and sense of well-being. Having
knowledge of the therapeutic qualities of colours can make you
home environment a place that will nurture your emotional health
and make it a place where you feel comfortable, confident and safe
Furthermore, you can choose to wear colours that will have a
impact on your emotional well-being. If, for example, you are enter
ing a situation where you fear a panic attack might strike, you ca
choose colours that calm. Similarly, if your attacks often strike whil
you are sleeping, choose colours for your bedroom (and even you
nightwear) that do the same.

*A Guide to Colours*

| | |
|---|---|
| red | physically stimulating, action-orientated, warm, cosy, vibrant, antidepressant |
| pink | emotionally soothing and calming, gently warming, uplifting |
| peach | warm, secure, glowing, creative, stimulating, an aid to digestion |
| yellow | uplifting, happy, bright, mentally stimulating |
| green | harmonising, relaxing, cooling, calming, restful to the mind |
| blue | cool, relaxing, calming to the mind |
| turquoise | refreshing, cooling, calming to the mind, youthfu |
| violet | dramatic, formal, spiritual, creative |
| brown | nurturing, earthy, supportive, practical |

aler tones of these colours will have a milder action, while richer, eeper tones will have a more powerful effect.

## Herbalism

Herbalism embraces the use of plants, in particular herbs, for healing. While herbs are used in many cultures, most specifically China and India, the tradition of Western medical herbalism is also a rich and varied one, calling upon folk remedies, ancient customs and practical experience, and combining this with new research, clinical training and diagnostic skills.

Herbal medicine is based on a holistic approach to health, like many other complementary medicines, and treatment will be undertaken after an assessment of your individual symptoms as well as your lifestyle and overall health, on both a physical and spiritual level.

Herbal medicine is designed to be gentle, stimulating our bodies to return to health by strengthening this systems as well as attacking the cause of the illness itself. Probably the most important principle of herbal medicine is that extracts are taken from the *whole* plant (or the whole of a part of the plant, like the leaves or the roots), not isolated or synthesised to perform specific functions.

Advice and treatment is always tailored to individual needs; because of this there is far less chance of having an adverse reaction to treatment. The aim of herbalism is to help the body to heal itself and to restore balanced health, not just to relieve the symptoms of the disorder being treated.

Herbalism is not a miracle cure and, like any other therapy, works best for specific conditions. Having said that, almost anyone can benefit from the prudent use of herbs as a form of restorative and preventative medicine. Herbs are a rich source of vitamins and minerals, aside from having healing properties, and can be an important part of your daily diet, eaten fresh, or perhaps drunk as a tisane. A herbal tonic is useful, for example, in the winter months, when fresh fruit and green vegetables are not such a regular part of our diets. Or something like echinacea or garlic can be taken daily to improve the general efficiency of the immune system.

Herbalism has a good record in the treatment of anxiety, depression, panic disorder, phobias, nervous problems and stress-related conditions. Interestingly, too, it is excellent for treating problems

associated with hormones (as in the menopause), so prudent use ‹
herbs that balance the body can prevent conditions in which pan
attacks can arise.

Other than purchasing herbal teas at your local health food shop,
would be wise to consult a registered medical herbalist before takir
herbs for medicinal purposes. The majority of herbs are safe for mo
people, but there are also many contraindications – especially if yc
are pregnant, very old or very young, or suffer from a long-term ‹
chronic condition. Always remember that herbs can be a powerf‹
form of healing and must be taken in moderation.

Now we'll take a look at the best herbs for panic disorder.

*St John's Wort*

The gentle properties of the herb *Hypericum perforatum* – con
monly known as St John's wort – have been known for centurie:
but it is only recently that scientists have been able to provide conclu
sive proof of its benefits.

Recent studies have shown that standardised extracts of St John
wort are as effective as traditionally prescribed antidepressants with
out the associated side-effects, and can relieve the symptoms of mil
to moderate depression in a wide range of conditions including: Sea
sonal Affective Disorder (SAD), pre-menstrual syndrome, fatigu
and the menopause.

*Kava Kava*

Kava kava (*Piper methysticum*) is a member of the black pepper plar
family originating from the South Sea Islands. In recent studies, star
dardised extracts of kava kava have proved to be effective in relievin
feelings of anxiety and stress, and can ease insomnia and other ne‹
vous-related disorders. At the time of writing this book kava kava i
available for purchase in the UK although there is the possibility the
this product could become available only on prescription in the future

Research carried out in Germany suggests that standardised kav
kava extract can help promote a sense of calm and tranquillity, whil
keeping a clear mind.

It appears to relax and strengthen rather than sedate, which make
it an ideal choice for busy people. It can be safely taken alongside S
John's wort.

Pregnant or breast-feeding women should not take kava kava.

## Valerian

Valerian is traditionally used to encourage relaxation and sleep, and acts as a mild and toning sedative. This strong-smelling herb is used to relieve conditions that have been induced by anxiety and nervous tension. It helps to restore the nervous system and calm the heart, and is used to treat anxiety, confusion, migraines, insomnia and depression with anxiety. Its overall effect on the body – and the nervous system in particular – makes it a good choice for panic disorder. Although many attacks do not take place in consciously stressful circumstances, the underlying stress, anxiety and fear cause them to occur. Valerian eases that state of mind and may, therefore, be a good preventative.

## Chamomile

A gentle, restorative herb, the effects of chamomile can be dramatic when it is taken on a daily basis. Calming and soothing, it helps to ease anxiety, tension, headaches and insomnia. It also helps with digestive complaints associated with stress and panic.

Many sufferers claim that sipping a cup of chamomile tea while in a warm bath is enough to divert an attack, when they feel one impending.

## Avena sativa

Avena sativa (oats) is an excellent herb for the nervous system. It has a number of relevant properties, including acting as a nervine tonic and antidepressant, relaxing the heart and circulation.

Oats is one of the best remedies for 'feeding' the nervous system, especially when under stress. It is considered in cases of nervous debility and exhaustion when associated with depression and anxiety of any nature. It may be used with most of the other nervines, both relaxant and stimulating, to strengthen the whole of the nervous system. It is also used in cases of general debility.

## Homeopathy

Homeopathy is a system of medicine that supports the body's own healing mechanism, using specially prepared remedies. It is 'energy' medicine, in that it works with the body's vital force to encourage healing and to ensure that all body systems are working at optimum level. Homeopathy is often confused with herbalism – partly, perhaps, because some of the remedies are made from herbs. However, herbalists use material concentrations of plants, while homeopathi remedies use plants, minerals and even some animal products as base. They are prepared through a process known as 'potentisation' t bring out their subtle healing properties.

We know from modern physics that our seemingly solid bodies ar just dense fields of energy. A disturbance in our energy field can giv rise to disease, and a potent form of energy can rebalance us Homeopathy uses 'potentised' remedies to rebalance our body' subtle energy system. Once this is back in balance, the immune sys tem and all the other interconnected systems in our body start func tioning better.

The term 'homeopathy' comes from the Greek, meaning 'simila suffering'. It reflects the key principle behind the homeopathi method – that a substance can cure the symptoms in an ill perso that it is capable of *causing* in a healthy person.

A Dr Hahnemann developed the first principles of homeopath back in the 19th century. He believed that symptoms and signs of a illness were in fact attempts on the part of the body to heal itself, s that when a substance capable of producing a similar symptom 'pic ture' to that of the disease was used, it would encourage a powerfu strengthening of the defence mechanism. A homeopath, therefore must study the entire symptom picture in order to get a complet 'map' of the disease and prescribe the correct remedy. Often, it is th symptoms that seem almost incidental, strange or rare that are th most valuable to the homeopathic practitioner, for they give the dis ease its own particular character and thus suggest the correc remedy.

Homeopathy can be used to treat everyone, from babies to th elderly. It is completely safe for people of all ages, and excellent fo dealing with the effects of stress, post-traumatic stress disorder, pho bias, depression, anxiety and panic.

Treatment must be constitutional – in other words, appropriate fo your individual needs, according to the symptom picture that you present to your homeopath during a consultation.

Effects can be dramatic, although for longer-standing, chroni panic disorders you can expect treatment to carry on for severa months. The best thing about homeopathy is that it will right any imbalances – hormonal, thyroid, blood sugar – leaving you in a state of good emotional and physical health. Under these conditions anic attacks are less likely.

There are remedies that can be taken for 'acute' situations that arise - that is, something that requires immediate intervention and is of an immediate or emergency nature. For example:

For stage fright, or fear of public speaking – **Lycopodium**
  *(particularly good where there is great apprehension, although*
    *you perform well once you have started)*
**Gelsemium**, when you feel weak at the knees
**Argentum nit**, when fear is dramatic enough to cause diarrhoea
For panic – **Arnica** in the first instance
For paralysing fear – **Opium**
If you still feel weak and shaky after the panic has
    subsided – **Gelsemium**

There are also a multitude of remedies appropriate for anxiety, but these are best administered by a homeopath on a constitutional basis.

## Massage
The therapeutic effects of massage are well documented and, although sceptics insist that any health benefits derive from an improved sense of well-being, rather than any biological response by the body, there is no doubt that massage works on many levels to improve overall health.

Massage is one of the oldest, simplest forms of therapy and is a system of stroking, pressing and kneading different areas of the body to relieve pain, relax, stimulate, and tone the body. Massage does much more than make you feel good, it also works on the soft tissues (the muscles, tendons and ligaments) to improve muscle tone. Although it largely affects those muscles just under the skin, it is believed that it also reaches the deeper layers of muscles, and possibly even the organs themselves. Massage also stimulates blood circulation and assists the lymphatic system (which runs parallel to the circulatory system), improving elimination of toxic waste throughout the body.

Here are some of the proven physical effects of massage:
● It is known to increase the circulation of blood and flow of lymph. The direct mechanical effect of rhythmically applied manual

71

pressure and movement used in massage can dramaticall increase the rate of blood flow. Also, the stimulation of nerv receptors causes the blood vessels (by relaxation) to dilate, which also encourages blood flow.

- For the whole body to be healthy, the individual cells must be healthy. These cells are dependent on an abundant supply o blood and lymph, because these fluids supply nutrients and oxy gen and carry away wastes and toxins.

- It causes changes in the blood. The oxygen capacity of the bloo can increase by 10-15 per cent after massage.

- Massage can help loosen contracted, shortened muscles and car stimulate weak, flaccid muscles. This muscle balancing can help posture and promote more efficient movement. Massage doe: not directly increase muscle strength, but it can speed recover from the fatigue that occurs after exercise. Massage also provide: a gentle stretching action to both the muscles and connective tis sues that surround and support the muscles and many other part: of the body, which helps keep these tissues elastic.

- It increases the body's secretions and excretions. There is a prover increase in the production of gastric juices, saliva, and urine There is also increased excretion of nitrogen, inorganic phos phorus, and sodium chloride (salt). This suggests that the meta bolic rate (the utilisation of absorbed material by the body's cells increases.

- Massage balances the nervous system by soothing or stimulating it, depending on what your body needs at the time of the massage

- Massage directly improves the function of the sebaceous (oil) anc sweat glands which keep the skin lubricated, clean and cooled Tough, inflexible skin can become softer and more supple.

- By indirectly or directly stimulating nerves that supply interna organs, blood vessels of the organs dilate and allow greater blood supply to them.

Massage has been proven to help a wide range of health conditions. Well-documented studies abound: medical school students at the University of Medicine and Dentistry of New Jersey – New Jersey Medical School who were massaged before an exam showed a sig- nificant decrease in anxiety and respiratory rates, as well as a signifi- cant increase in white blood cells and natural killer cell activity, suggesting a benefit to the immune system.

Regular massage can improve well-being, encourage a state of relaxation, encourage overall health, improve self-image (the power of touch is well documented) and ease the symptoms of panic, anxiety and stress. It can be undertaken alongside any other therapies, and used in conjunction with aromatherapy essential oils for enhanced effect.

I would suggest that anyone suffering from regular panic attacks would benefit from massage, and on a regular basis.

## Meditation

The word *meditation* comes from the Latin word 'mederi', meaning 'to heal'. Western medicine has been slow to catch on to the benefits of meditation, but research has now shown that it can slow your heart rate, reduce negative emotions and produce a sense of calm. Meditation is a tool to make us aware of the peace within us, a place that the outside world cannot touch or influence. This is crucial for anyone suffering from panic attacks. If you become experienced at finding a place of peace, you can retreat there when you experience an attack or feel one coming on. What's more, if you reach the state of total relaxation that meditation offers, you are far less likely to suffer an attack.

The practice of meditation not only helps us relax by relaxing the mind first, but it also teaches us about our thinking patterns and how we can control them.

Meditation should ideally be learned from an experienced instructor, but you can practise it at home. Always try to meditate at the same time each day and in the same place if possible. Breathe gently and with a regular rhythm from the abdomen. Begin with five minutes or so of deep breathing, then breathe a little more gently.

The form of meditation you choose will be unique to you. The idea is simply to clear and purify the mind and allow your own natural energy or life force to flow within you. It may help to visualise this. There is no wrong way to meditate. Try this simple exercise to begin with:

1. Sit cross-legged on the floor with your hands outstretched and your palms facing upwards. Sit comfortably, with your back straight. You can meditate with your eyes opened or closed, whatever feels best to you.
2. Breathe in and out five times.

3. Aim to reach a state of inner peace.
4. Continue to breathe evenly while you focus your mind on you mantra (a special calming word or phrase), or on the drifting o your thoughts.
5. Do not hold on to any stray thoughts. Let them go and watch then pass.
6. Breathe slowly and calmly and allow your mind and body to rela completely.
7. Focus all of your attention inwards.
8. After a while, try to breathe more deeply.
9. Open your eyes and take a few minutes to rest.

## Nutritional Therapies

Our understanding of vitamins and minerals – and other micronu trients, compounds and elements – and their role in the body ha improved dramatically over the last few decades. We now know tha 'micronutrition' – or the vitamins, minerals and other health-giving components of our food, such as amino acids, fibre, enzymes, and lipids – is crucial to life, and that by manipulating our nutritional intake we can not only ensure good health and address ailments, but also take control of our emotional health, which is intrinsically linked to our physical well-being.

Nutrition has changed from being a mainly doctor-led dietary ther-apy, also called clinical nutrition, into a more profound theory of health based on treating the patient as a whole (holistic health), and looking for deficiencies which may be causing illness, which are spe-cific to each individual.

There is a wealth of evidence that nutrition plays a part in panic attacks and anxiety, and there are also many foods that can help to calm the nervous system and restore emotional equilibrium. In Chapter Six we'll look at the elements of a healthy diet. Here, how-ever, we'll look at the specific supplements that can make a difference to the way you feel and how your body copes with stress and other environmental factors which may lead to panic attacks.

### B vitamins

The B-vitamin complex is essential for the healthy function of the nervous system, and there is some evidence that deficiency may be at the root of panic disorder. In the modern world, many of us are eficient in these vitamins, largely because they are stripped out of so many foods in the refining process.

One study has shown that B-vitamin supplementation improved all of 20 patients who were suffering from symptoms of panic and neurosis. In particular, vitamin B3 has been shown to have anti-anxiety, anti-aggressive, anti-convulsive and muscle-relaxant properties. Definitely worth supplementing on a daily basis.

### Selenium
Selenium levels in the food chain are very low in some parts of the world, including the UK. One study showed that increasing selenium intake reduced anxiety, depression and fatigue, as well as a general elevation of mood. Selenium should be taken as part of a good antioxidant (vitamins A, C, E and zinc) supplement.

### Calcium and Magnesium
Both of these minerals act as natural tranquillisers, helping to relieve anxiety, tension, nervousness, muscular spasms and tics. They are best taken in combination.

### Iron
There is some evidence that iron deficiency can increase the risk of panic attacks. Choose a good liquid supplement, such as Floradix, which is a natural source of iron. It's worth noting, too, that if you are taking tricyclic antidepressants, they can, in the presence of low iron levels in the blood, increase the risk of developing anxiety symptoms.

### Chromium
Chromium deficiency can produce nervousness, shakiness and other general symptoms of anxiety. It's often deficient in people who consume large quantities of refined sugars, and who drink a lot of alcohol. Chromium is a trace element, necessary for controlling the GTF (glucose tolerance factor), which regulates blood sugar. As blood sugar is almost certainly implicated in panic disorder, this is another supplement worth taking. It's found in high quantities in brewer's yeast.

### Vitamin C
Vitamin C is not only for colds! This vitamin is necessary for proper function of the adrenal glands, and brain chemistry. In large doses it

can have a powerful tranquillising effect, and is known to decreas
anxiety.

*Zinc*
This mineral has a calming effect on the central nervous system, an
also has antioxidant properties, which means that it can help to pre
vent and repair the destructive and damaging effects of stress an
anxiety on the body.

*The Foods We Eat*
Food can also have a dramatic effect on our moods and emotiona
state (as well, of course, as on our physical state). The following are
noteworthy for their effect on the nervous system and other system:
affected by panic:

- Mango: Mangoes are rich in antioxidants, which help to repair the
  destructive effects of panic, anxiety and stress on the body. They
  also contain an acid that helps bowel health.
- Apricots: Another good source of antioxidants. Fresh is best, but
  if you go for the dried version, make sure they are not sulphured.
- Bananas: These contain potassium, required for nerve functioning and the health of the heart and brain. They help to keep
  blood pressure at a healthy level, and encourage the action of the
  kidneys.
- Apples: Another rich source of antioxidants, and also great
  detoxifiers.
- Broccoli: This is an excellent source of magnesium, which is
  known as the 'anti-stress' mineral. It also helps the body use antioxidants. Broccoli also contains anti-cancer compounds, which is
  important given the link between cancer and stress.
- Nuts and seeds: These contain EFAs (essential fatty acids), as well
  as calcium and magnesium, which help to maintain a healthy nervous system. Nuts and seeds also contain zinc, which is an important anti-stress nutrient.
- Tuna: Although all fish is healthy, and a good source of healthy
  oils, tuna in particular has powerful anti-inflammatory fats that
  encourage the health of the nervous system, balance hormones
  and help to prevent heart disease.
- Watermelon: This seasonal fruit contains high levels of potassium,
  which is required for the function of the nervous system and the

heart and brain. It's also important for stable blood pressure.

- Red onions: These contain several compounds that work in different ways. They are a good source of powerful antioxidants, but they also contain acids that support the liver and help to excrete toxins. Other properties include being antibiotic, anti-viral and anti-candida (the organism that can lead to thrush).

Grapes are great detoxifiers, and contain antioxidants. Go for red grapes if you can.

Celery helps to calm the nerves, perhaps because it is so rich in calcium, and it's also helpful for the treatment of stomach ulcers and other digestive complaints.

Strawberries are known to combat high blood pressure, and their high iron content will help you to cope better with fatigue. The link between iron deficiency and panic attacks is also relevant here.

- Brown rice is a powerful detoxifier, and has a beneficial effect on the digestive tract, being both soothing and cleansing. It's also recommended for lowering blood pressure. Rice is also rich in the B vitamins, which are essential for nervous system health.

Oats: Not only are these rich in B vitamins, for a healthy nervous system, but they supply silicon for healthy arterial walls. What's more, they contain calcium, potassium and magnesium, all of which are important in times of stress. Studies show that oats help to combat high levels of blood cholesterol and regulate body fats, but they also appear to have a favourable effect on sugar metabolism, which is important given the link between panic attacks and blood sugar.

- Avocados are an almost complete food, as they supply protein, carbohydrates, and healthy fats. They are rich in potassium and a good source of vitamins A, B-complex, C and E. They act as an antioxidant in the body, helping to prevent damage caused by stress of any nature.

## Positive Affirmations

Much the same as visualisation (see page 83), positive affirmations have a convincing effect on the brain which acts to override negative emotions and self-image. The idea is that you create phrases that you repeat over and over, thereby affirming your own positive self-image. Another word for this type of treatment is 'positive self-talk'. The repetitive nature of the sayings is a type of 'mind training', almost hypnotising yourself into a new belief. Affirmations are also useful in eme gency situations. If you are feeling panicky or anxious, you can repe a positive phrase that you have used in the past. Keep a good store positive affirmations, and use them regularly to retrain your though processes. Used on a regular basis, they can become a self-fulfillin prophecy. Try some of the following:

- Every day, in every way, I'm getting better and better (this was fir coined by Emil Cou, a French hypnotherapist).
- I am relaxed, I am calm, I am at peace.
- I am free of panic, I can release the past.
- I am happy and content.
- I am loved and I am a good person (because ...)
- The more you fill yourself with these positive thoughts, the mor you come to believe them and make use of them to alleviate stress anxiety and panic.

## Reflexology

Reflexology involves stimulating, massaging and applying pres sure to points on the hands and feet which correspond to variou systems and organs throughout the body to stimulate the body' own healing system. These points are called 'reflex points', and each point corresponds to a different body part or function.

Reflexologists believe that applying pressure to these refle points can improve the health of the body and mind. Depending on the points chosen, reflexology can be used to ease tension reduce inflammation, relieve congestion, improve circulation and eliminate toxins from the body.

Like many other complementary therapists, reflexologists do no claim to cure anything; rather, they aim to stimulate the body to heal itself. They do this by working on the physical body to stimu late healing at the physical, mental and emotional levels.

Pressure applied to nerve endings can influence all the body sys tems, including the circulation and lymphatic systems. Improve ments in circulation and the lymphatic system result in improved body functioning, because nutrients and oxygen are transported more efficiently round the body, and toxins are eliminated with greater ease. Energy pathways are opened up so that the body is able to work more effectively, and harmony, or 'homeostasis', is restored.

Reflexologists believe that the body is divided into ten vertical zones or channels, five on the left and five on the right. Each zone runs from the head right down to the reflex areas on the hands and feet and from the front through to the back of the body. All the body parts within any one zone are linked by the nerve pathways and are mirrored in the corresponding reflex zone on the hands and feet. By applying pressure to a reflex point or area, the therapist can stimulate or rebalance the energy in the related zone.

Each zone is a channel for energy (called *chi* in Eastern disciplines). Stimulating or working any zone in the foot, by applying pressure with the thumbs and fingers, affects the entire channel throughout the body. For example, working a zone on the foot along the channel on which the kidneys lie will release vital energy that may be blocked somewhere else in that channel, such as in the eyes. Working the kidney reflex area on the foot will therefore revitalise and balance the entire channel.

Reflexology is an excellent whole-body system, and can be used both to prevent illness and to encourage the body to heal. It is particularly useful for stress and related disorders and emotional disorders, as well as digestive problems, circulatory disorders, menstrual problems, insomnia, fatigue, and most chronic and acute illnesses. Because so many systems in the body are affected and influenced by panic, this type of whole-body treatment can be profoundly useful. Because it relaxes and rejuvenates, it can also help to prevent attacks in susceptible people.

Beware, however: because the body is being encouraged to heal itself, some symptoms can be 'thrown up'. In most cases, this is nothing to worry about – it simply represents a 'healing crisis', whereby some symptoms appear to become worse before they get better. Most people will not experience any symptoms, but you should be aware that the following can occur:

- cold-like symptoms such as a runny nose, as any catarrh or sinus congestion is cleared
- a cough, as mucus is cleared from the lungs and respiratory passages
- more frequent emptying of the bladder
- more frequent emptying of the bowels
- flatulence
- headache

- increased sweating
- skin rash – some skin conditions may get worse before they get better
- yawning
- tiredness

The main parts of the body are reflected in the following areas of the feet:

| | |
|---|---|
| the head and neck | – within the toe areas |
| the spine | – down the inner border of both feet |
| the chest | – between the levels of the shoulder girdle and the diaphragm on both feet |
| the abdomen | – below the level of the diaphragm to just above the pad of the heel on both feet |
| the pelvis | – over the pad of the heel |
| the limbs | – on the outer side of the feet |
| the reproductive glands | – on the sides of the feet near and over the ankles |
| the lymphatic system and breasts | – on the top of the feet |

Generally speaking, the best reflexology treatment for panic attacks would focus on the areas corresponding with the nervous system. You can do this at home, or have it done by a registered practitioner. If you do choose to try this at home, ask your partner or a friend to follow this procedure:

1. Massage both feet, pressing your thumb into the solar plexus point on both feet (in the centre of the foot, beneath the balls of the feet, where it indents slightly). This relaxes the central nervous system.

2. Press your thumb into and along the spine area (the inner border) of the foot, which improves circulation and energy to the central nervous system.

3. Press your thumb into and along the side of the spine (closer to the sole) to improve circulation and energy to the peripheral nervous system.

4. Massage and press your thumb firmly into the big toe, and pull it gently. This helps to improve circulation and nerve conductivity.

5. When you encounter tender spots, gently massage these until the discomfort ceases.

## Relaxation

Research has shown that mental activity has a direct effect on the body – that a relaxed mind can produce significant physical benefits. In other words, if your mind is relaxed, your body will be, too.

It has been found that relaxation can slow heart rate, lower blood pressure, and regulate breathing and metabolic rate. It also reduces adrenaline levels and allows the immune system to function more efficiently. Stress is a normal and necessary part of life, which provides motivation, stimulation and the drive to meet challenges with enthusiasm. Too much stress, however, as we know, is harmful. The key to controlling our stress levels is relaxation. What's more, relaxation can control unwanted thoughts by creating a physical and emotional sense of peace. Everyone will benefit from relaxation on a daily basis.

True relaxation is a healing process that focuses the mind and body. You will learn how to control and resolve the effects of stress and panic rather than suppressing them with short-term measures, such as alcohol or overeating. Relaxation is a skill. Practised correctly, it can both prevent and treat disease, and improve your sense of well-being. Once you have learned how to do it, relaxation is a state that you can bring about wherever you are and whatever you are doing.

Therapists use and teach a number of different types of physical and mental relaxation techniques, and in some cases induce very deep relaxation.

### Active Muscular Relaxation

In this exercise, you tense your muscles and then release them to feel the physical and mental release that accompanies each movement. You will be taught how to work around your body, possibly starting with an arm or leg and focusing on every detail, including fingers and toes. A therapist can guide you around your body, asking you to

81

hold various muscles for about 10 seconds. At the end of the session which usually lasts for 20-30 minutes, he or she will tell you that the session is ending and that when you open your eyes and stretch you will feel relaxed and refreshed.

*Passive Muscular Relaxation*

This is similar to the tense-release exercise, but instead of tensing a muscle group you focus your attention on the group, acknowledge the tension already held there and then release it. You may be asked to imagine a slow wave of relaxation washing through your muscles, lengthening and expanding them, loosening any points of tension.

## Self-help Groups

There is no doubt that self-help and support groups are enormously helpful in coping with panic attacks and other forms of anxiety. Indeed, there is an abundance of medical literature confirming the merits of this approach to treatment. Being a member of a group means that you never have to feel you are alone with your anxiety problem, and it also means that you have the responsibility to help others, as well as to receive help yourself. The former is empowering, which raises self-esteem; the latter is invaluable. Tips and methods of coping can be shared, as well as experiences with various therapies and medications. What's more, talking with others unlocks the stigma surrounding panic disorder, and is one of the keys to emotional health and self-esteem.

A group situation reminds us that we are not alone in our pain and fear, and that there are always others to comfort us. According to the famous psychotherapist Carl Jung, when we share sorrows or difficulties, we become 'wounded healers'. We are experts who can mutually console one another because we have intimate experience with a particular illness and its manifestations.

Most internet sites that deal with the subject of panic disorder, or charitable organisations that deal with anxiety, will be able to provide a list of local support groups. Otherwise, talk to your GP or check the noticeboard at your local surgery. If you can't find something convenient, consider starting your own.

# Visualisation

This technique can be easily learned and used to great effect. Visualisation is the conscious use of the imagination to create images that you can use to heal or change aspects of your life. It can help to deepen the relaxation process and overcome many mental and emotional problems. It is often goal-directed, which means you set yourself a mental goal such as 'I feel calm and in control' or 'I do not panic', and your mind learns to accept it. Relaxation therapists encourage you to use the skill to picture yourself overcoming a problem or an illness (such as panic disorder) and to replace negative and destructive emotions with positive, life-enhancing ones.

Visualisation uses the power of the mind to enhance the benefits of physical relaxation. The brain is divided into two hemispheres: the left, which is concerned with logic and reason, and the right, which relates to creativity, imagination and the emotions. Most of the time we use the left side to work, study and cope with daily life. The right side is used much less, but any images which we create in it are believed to be directly linked to physical responses in the body. So remembering an embarrassing situation can bring on all the symptoms of the stress experienced in the initial situation. Given that most of us have such intense and strong memories of anything we consider to be traumatic, it's extremely useful to learn the balancing art of positive visualisation. Soothing or positive images can provoke a corresponding sense of calm or well-being in the body.

Visualisation encourages right-brain activity and uses the images it provides to override destructive effects wrought by the left side. It is based on the belief that imagination is stronger than intellect. If you give your mind a positive image, it will accept it, providing the image is strong and believable.

For visualisation to be effective it should, ideally, be practised on a regular basis. When you are in the bath, for example, or on the train on the way to work. There is a build-up effect, and you can call upon the mental images that you create when you feel an impending attack, or when you are in the throes of one.

# Yoga

Yoga encourages flexibility, relaxation skills, and good breathing. Used therapeutically, yoga can help with the following: muscle and joint mobility, flexibility, breathing disorders, musculo-skeletal pain, nervous system and endocrine disorders, digestive problems, fatigue, insomnia and stress-related conditions. It's an excellent form of relaxation, essential for sufferers of panic attacks in part because it focuses on breathing, but also because it encourages all-round holistic health.

The word *yoga* means 'unity' or 'oneness', and is derived from the Sanskrit word 'yug', which means 'to join'. In spiritual terms this refers to the union of the individual consciousness with the universal consciousness. On a practical level, yoga is a means of balancing and harmonising the body, mind and emotions and is a tool that allows us to withdraw from the chaos of the world and find a quiet space within. It utilises the innate life force within the body and teaches how to tap into, harness and direct it skilfully. To achieve this, yoga uses movement, breath, posture, relaxation and meditation in order to establish a healthy, vibrant and balanced approach to living.

Yoga exercises are comprised of *asanas*, or postures, which involve stretching, bending, turning and relaxation. Each posture has a specific therapeutic effect.

There are six main groups of yoga postures: standing, inverted, twisting, backbend, forward bend and side bend.

- standing – improves efficiency of the muscular, circulatory, respiratory, digestive, reproductive, endocrine and nervous systems
- inverted – balances the endocrine system and metabolism, enhances thinking power and revitalises internal organs
- twisting – aids digestion, helps relieve back pain, improves intercostal breathing
- backbend – invigorates; encourages deep breathing
- forward bend – improves blood circulation, aids digestion, calms emotions
- side bend – stimulates main organs such as the liver, kidney, stomach, spleen

There are yoga classes available throughout the country, and many teachers are happy to provide lessons in the comfort of your own home. As a basis for good health, for improved emotional and physi-

al functioning, and for relaxation, yoga is recommended to all
panic-attack sufferers.

# Chapter Five

# What to Do during an Attack

Most of the therapies discussed in Chapter Four focus on long-term treatment options which help to ensure that you overcome panic attacks and other anxiety-related symptoms for good. Once embarked on a course of treatment, you should see significant improvement. If you don't, there is no harm is changing therapies or adding another therapy alongside.

But while treatment is beginning to take effect, or in the event of a relapse, it is helpful to have some tools at your disposal to ease an attack, reduce its duration, or even ward it off completely. Let's take a look at some of the best ideas on offer.

## Homeopathic Remedies

On page 71 we discussed remedies for use in a crisis. The following steps may also help:

In the first instance – **Arnica**
If you are feeling shock or intense trauma – **Aconite**
If your symptoms come on after a bereavement or loss of
a loved – **oneIgnatia**
If your attack is triggered by anxiety about a new situation, or
when having to perform in front of an audience – **Lycopodium**
If your symptoms come on after overwork or
overindulgence – **Nux vomica**
If you feel as though your nervous system is out of control,
mainly because of overwork, and you find it difficult to let
go or relax – **Tarentula**
For great anxiety and restlessness, combined with fear – **Arsenicum**
If your symptoms are accompanied by a sensation of floating,
levitating or losing your identity – **Valeriana**

These remedies can be taken at the first sign of an impending attack every two hours for up to 10 doses. Aconite can be taken every 15 minutes when an attack is imminent, and throughout.

## Flower Essences

Dr Bach's Rescue Remedy (see page 64) is the best choice, as it contains flower essences designed to deal with all of the side-effects and symptoms of panic attacks. Put a few drops in a glass of water and sip, or put it directly on your tongue, as often as required, for fairly instant relief. Many panic attack sufferers carry a bottle with them at all times, and swear by its helpful effects.

## Herbalism

Most herbs have a cumulative effect and work over time, but there are some that have a fairly instant effect, as well as working at a deeper level to promote healing.

Chamomile, motherwort and passionflower all promote relaxation and aid in the prevention of panic attacks. They can all be taken in a variety of forms, but it's worth taking one, or a blend of two or all three at the first sign of an attack, and even during an attack to help to relieve symptoms. A warm cup of chamomile tea, for example, can soothe and calm you down, which is often enough to stave off an attack.

Skullcap and valerian can be taken at bedtime to promote sleep and prevent panic attacks during the night.

## Aromatherapy

Dab a drop of lavender oil at the base of your nose, and rub gently into your temples, diluted in a little olive oil or grapeseed oil. This will help to calm and relax you.

Similarly, massaging your temples with any of the sedative oils (see page 58), diluted in a light carrier oil, will help to ease symptoms.

## Tactile Stimulation

Anything that helps you back into your body and into a composed state of mind will help, and there is plenty of evidence to show that ouch can do just this. Massage your shoulders and temples, gently tap your knees, keep a loose elastic band around your wrist and, when you feel panic advancing, snap it hard. You can also try pinching yourself – hard. Even splashing your face with cold water will help. Anything that stimulates your sense of touch will reassure you that you are real, present and still living and breathing. It will also help to distract you from your anxiety.

## Stimulating Your Tastebuds

In the throes of an attack, some sufferers claim that sucking or chewing something tart provides a jolt that brings them back into focus. Suck a lemon or a lemon drop, for example. Strong mints should have the same effect, and will momentarily elevate blood sugar, which may be dipping.

## Talk to Yourself

Self-talk, either in the form of positive affirmations or as a soothing narrative to get you back on track, is undoubtedly a positive healing tool. Talk can be very reassuring, and you need this to control your thoughts and move them away from the sensation of panic.

Take power. Take control. Consider the fact that a panic attack is just an expression of your body and mind. You can regain control. Remember that an attack normally lasts between 30 seconds and 3 minutes. Talk to yourself and try to keep things in perspective: 'I am in control. This panic is nothing more than a momentary, passing feeling. I can get through it.'

Every time you get through a panic attack, manage to control some of the symptoms, or lessen the duration, you have taken a step forward. Celebrate your victories and remind yourself of them should you experience another attack. You can get through it. You will. You will be stronger for it, and you will regain control.

We need to see how our thoughts create so much of our fear, which in turn creates many of our symptoms. Once we see this, we can see how the anxiety and/or panic are actually *reactions to* our thoughts, and not the other way round. Our thoughts are not a reaction to the anxiety and/or panic. Once we can see this, we can reverse our thinking from 'What if...?' to 'I can handle whatever comes my way!' This is the way to power and freedom.

## Breathe

To help manage an acute attack using breathing techniques (se
page 65), inhale slowly to the count of four, hold your breath for
count of four, exhale slowly to a count of four, and then do nothin
for a count of four. Repeat this sequence until the attack subside
Remind yourself that panic attacks last for a limited amount of tim
and that this one, too, will pass.

In extreme situations you may feel that your airway is blocke
almost as though you are being strangled. This is normal, after
build-up of anxiety. In such a situation, breathing correctly may b
quite a challenge. One way to combat the attack is to imagine tha
the air you're taking in is clearing away the blockage. With eac
breath, more air is able to filter through, until finally your breath
become deeper and your body relaxes again.

Remember that panic attacks are all about fear. By concentratin
on your breathing and using your imagination to free your breath
associating this action with the release of fear – breathing will pro
vide both a focus and a respite in times of panic.

## Run

This may sound ridiculous, particularly if you feel a bit out of cor
trol, but in the throes of a panic attack, adrenaline is surging. Rur
ning – and fast – helps to disperse the adrenaline quickl
negating its harmful effects. Exercise also changes the nature c
your breathing, which will undoubtedly be affected during a
attack, and encourages the release of endorphins (natural painki
lers and mood-elevating hormones). If you can't physically rur
imagine yourself bursting out of the door and into the fresh ai
and high-tailing it away from the situation.

## Use Autogenic Training Techniques

Imagine your limbs, and then the other parts of your body, feelin
warm and heavy. Hold on to that feeling, and remember it. Thi
powerful technique encourages your body to respond in kind to th
memory of feeling this way, and to become relaxed (see page 59).

sychotherapist Dr Herbert Spiegel has discovered something alled the 'eye roll', which he found was the most obvious trigger of a ance state. He discovered that if you can see the whites of someo-e's eyes easily when he is asked to roll his pupils upwards, he can nter a hypnotic state.

. On the count of one, allow your eyes to roll up.
. On the count of two, take a deep breath and hold it.
. On the count of three, relax as you close your eyes, and imagine yourself floating. Allow your breathing to become more quiet and easy.

'his takes you into the trance state and, when you are ready, you can ise the three-count backwards to come out of this state. In other vords:

. On three, allow your eyes to roll back downwards.
. On two, take a deep breath and hold it.
. On one, open your eyes and come out of the trance.

t takes only a few minutes to hypnotise yourself, although it's worth xperimenting to make sure that you can do it, rather than depend-ng on it as a quick-fix during an attack. You can experiment with your iypnotic control by trying the following:

Close your eyes and imagine a flowing feeling extending into your eft hand. Touch the middle finger of your left hand with the middle inger of your right hand. Tell yourself that you cannot possibly keep jour left hand in your lap. It is floating upwards by itself like a balloon. Open your eyes and attempt to push the left hand down with the ight. With practice, you will find that it floats back up again by itself.

The goal of self-hypnosis is to teach yourself to master your symp-oms rather than expecting them to vanish all by themselves.

## Meditate

Choose to find a place of peace within yourself through meditation, or simply release your mind from the situation and sit back and watch jour thoughts go by. Let them go, one by one – you can always ana-yse them later, once your attack is over. With this knowledge, you will be much more in control during the next attack, as you know what to expect. Meditation is a great tool for self-awareness, and brings with it an inherent sense of peace.

Meditate on your breathing, if that will help. Try the following exercise:

- Visualise your thoughts as a mass of bubbles. Exhale slowly through your mouth and, as you do, imagine all of these thought bubbles drifting away.
- Redirect your attention to your nostrils. Breathe in and out through your nose and, as you do, visualise the air passing through your nostrils, always under your control.
- Concentrate on exhaling in a long, smooth motion, letting the inhalation take care of itself.
- If your mind starts to wander, don't give up. Simply re-focus your attention on your nostrils and try to let the sensation of breathing fill your mind and consciousness.

Try this exercise during an attack, or when you feel one coming on. Also, practise it daily until you feel yourself breathing naturally, all of the time.

## Remember That You Are Not Alone

It may sound trite, but an awful lot of successful, even famous people suffer or have suffered from anxiety and panic attacks. Remind yourself that others feel and have felt the way that you do, and have overcome the condition. It's not a sign of weakness to suffer from panic attacks, and more and more people are admitting to having had them at some point in their lives. It's reassuring to know that high profile people have experienced the same symptoms, and gone on to great things. Remember this in the throes of an attack. For interest's sake, here are a few historical and famous people who have suffered from anxiety:

Charlotte Bronte
Sigmund Freud
Lord Olivier
Alfred Lord Tennyson

Robert Burns
Abraham Lincoln
John Steinbeck
W. B. Yeats

...Remember, you are not alone

# The Worst-Case Scenario

Panic is based on fear, and fear tends to be based on the potential unknown: 'What would happen if …?' 'It would be awful if …' 'I couldn't cope if …'

Look at it a different way. Sit down and think through all the awful, terrible things that could happen in the situation you fear, or in another panic attack itself. What is the worst-case scenario? If you confront your worst fears, accept them, and come up with an action plan, the reality is very likely to be far better. Nothing is ever as bad as we think it is going to be and, if we are prepared for the worst, getting through the attack will be that much easier.

# No Panic

The following tips will help you to cope in a panic attack.

- Try to keep a sense of perspective, and use any means you can to work through it. If you can do this, your next panic attack may well be the last one you ever have to deal with!
- Don't let the fear rule you. Don't think, 'What if…?' – Think 'I can master this!'
- Focus your mind on the present, not the future or the fear that it may hold.
- Don't judge your feelings. Accept them and take control.
- A panic attack is based on thoughts and feelings – and both of these are controllable. They are not actions. You can act. They cannot.
- Look at your thoughts. What are they saying to you that is scaring you?
- Remember, you have done it before and you can do it again.
- The more you work on controlling your thoughts, the more you can control them.
- You are the same person you were before the attack, and you are safe and all right.
- Remember that nothing terrible will happen, and that whatever does happen, you can handle it.
- What you are feeling is worrying and distressing, but it is not dangerous in any way.

- Anxiety reaches a peak and then it disperses.
- Take slow, deep breaths and concentrate on positive self thoughts: 'I can do this.' 'I am strong.' 'I am in control.' 'This can hurt me.' 'Slow down, start again.' 'It will be over soon.'


*Gina's Experience*
The first panic attack I remember was at the age of seven. I'd just sa an exam to get into a new school and, on the way home in the ca thinking it over, I realised I'd got something wrong. I'd spelt 'comb incorrectly, so the sentence read 'I come my hair'! I was stricken with terror, sweating, unable to tell anyone what I'd done. Of course, a cou ple of weeks later the letter came through saying I'd got into th school anyway, but I'd had a horrible time before then.

When I first moved to London, where I didn't know anyone, to take up a new job in publishing, I kept fainting on the tube. I mean, two o three times a week! I thought at first it must be due to poor air qualit down there, and wondered why other people didn't faint as well, bu when I mentioned it to a doctor she said they were panic attacks and that I should breathe into a brown paper bag when I started to fee dizzy. This wasn't very successful – I never seemed to have a bag ready at the right time.

One day at work – maybe after I'd been there about six months – got into a mess. I'd called someone for information on a book I wa editing, and at the end of our conversation he said he would be invoi cing the company for his time – which I had no authorisation for Also, I was working on a huge book with a very tight deadline and knew I would never get it finished in time. These problems, combined with other general anxiety, brought on such a huge panic attack one lunch hour that I actually hid under my desk with severe palpitations

Finally, I phoned my father and he calmly talked me through how to solve both work problems, which relieved my symptoms at the time.

Some years later, after a horrible break-in at my flat (the last of sev eral), I began to get panic attacks all the time. I was too scared to come home after dark except by taxi, and everything was getting on top of me. By chance, I found a wonderful counsellor and with her talked through all the background causes of my anxiety – the mas sive pressure I felt to succeed, for example. One piece of advice she

ve me for panic attacks is to find the nearest bed and lie down on it
have a nap if you can. It's not always practical, but even the thought
: doing this helps me feel more calm and centred.

## elping Someone Else Through an Attack

someone you know is in the throes of an attack, the best thing you
an do is to administer any of the remedies listed above (with their
pproval, of course), help them to focus on their breathing, and try
) distract them. Concentrate on encouraging the sufferer to feel bet-
:r about themselves, by praising their efforts, raising their self-
steem and making them feel more confident.

Use physical affection if you can. The power of touch is well docu-
ented and enormously reassuring. Ensure that the sufferer knows
at what they are feeling is completely normal for many, many peo-
le, and that it will pass. Try to dispel their fear by asking them to con-
entrate on positive images – events they have planned for the
ature, for example, or something successful that the sufferer has
one in the past, something they have achieved. The focus is on the
ositive, being calm, being supportive, and making sure the sufferer
els confident enough to take control.

# Chapter Six

# Positive Living: Making Lifestyle Changes

he environmental triggers of panic attacks cannot be understated, ut by taking different aspects of your lifestyle in hand you can make big difference to your chances of overcoming the condition for ood. If you smoke a great deal, drink too much coffee, get inadequate sleep and have a poor diet, for example, you will be setting ie stage for future attacks. In Chapter Two we discussed the various otential triggers and causes of panic attacks. All play their part. Vhat's more, you need to address elements of your life that might e causing stress, or putting you under unnecessary pressure. inally, you need to work on your self-image, so that you feel good bout yourself and able to cope with whatever life throws at you.

## Healthy Diet

Iealthy eating is crucial to both emotional and physical health, and a oor diet can have a dramatic effect on the way you feel on a day-to-ay basis. One of the most important things is to eat as many whole ods as possible, which ensures that your blood sugar is balanced. 's also a good idea to give up the idea of three meals a day, and eat ttle and often, which helps to keep blood sugar levels stable.

There is also some evidence that people suffering from panic disrder do better on a 'ketogenic' diet. This is essentially a low-carbohyrate diet, focusing more on proteins. Don't go wild, though. The idea ; not to avoid carbohydrates altogether (as many popular weightoss diets advise), but to make them a smaller proportion of your iet, and ensure that they are always 'whole' rather than refined. The deology behind this is simple: some carbohydrates (in particular, efined ones) cause blood sugar to soar and then plummet, which neans that adrenaline is released. Adrenaline promotes jitteriness nd other symptoms that can encourage or at least set the stage for panic attack.

So the answer is to replace processed foods with natural, unrefined alternatives. You also need to eat more fruits and vegetables, who grains, pulses, lean meats and low-fat dairy produce. This will mal a dramatic difference to your overall health, not just to the inciden of panic attacks.

Reduce or remove anything with artificial chemicals, in the form additives, preservatives, flavours or anything else. All of these pu strain on the body, in particular the liver, an organ which is so cruci for the stress response. What's more, these chemicals are a form environmental stress, which will raise your stress load even if oth aspects of your life are going well.

Given that digestion is dodgy under stress, it's important that tl foods you eat contain the best possible combination of nutrients.

The next step is to take supplements to balance some of tl unhealthy aspects of your diet, and to redress some of the dama caused by poor eating habits. Everyone, no matter what their sta of health, needs a good multi-vitamin and -mineral tablet.

Other supplements to consider are those listed on pages 75-6.

Aim to get adequate supplies of the following:
- healthy proteins, including very lean meats, fish, poultry, chees yoghurt, nuts, soya products (including tofu), pulses such as le tils, seeds (3 to 5 servings a day)
- fruit and vegetables and their juices. Anything goes. Rememb that the more colourful the vegetable, the more nutritious it ten to be (5 to 7 servings a day).
- carbohydrates for energy. Anything wholegrain or unrefine including pastas, bread, brown rice, grains (such as rye, barle corn, buckwheat), pulses, potatoes and whole-grain, sugar-fr cereals (4 to 9 servings a day).
- as much fluid as you can drink. Water is the most important part any diet. Between one and two litres is recommended, dependir on the weather.
- fibre-rich foods, to help encourage digestion and the optimu uptake of the nutrients in the foods you eat.

Eat organic when you can. There is still considerable debate abo whether or not organic foods are more nutritious, but there is r doubt that they are lower in the chemicals that place a strain c your system.

ut down on sweets, crisps, soft drinks and fast or 'junk' foods of ny nature. These not only tend to take the place of healthier alternatives, but they are also a key source of damaging chemicals and anti-nutrients'.

Make sure you eat lots of nutritious snacks. Keeping blood sugar levels stable throughout the day will help you to cope with stressful situations more efficiently, and lower your stress response significantly. Healthy snacks include fruit, vegetables, low-sugar live yoghurt, wholemeal toast, nuts, seeds, rice cakes, cheese, sugarless cereals, plain popcorn, humus and breadsticks.

Make sure you don't skip meals, which can send blood sugar levels plummeting and adrenaline soaring. Many people do not bother with breakfast, and a new survey shows that a huge number of people skip meals because of the frantic pace of their lives. The research, by the supermarket chain Sainsbury's, found that nearly 70 per cent of people regularly miss at least one meal a day. For more than a third of these people, the meal they miss is breakfast. Six out of ten people surveyed said they were simply too busy to stop to eat.

A healthy diet doesn't mean monotonous, tasteless meals. Experiment with a variety of different herbs and spices, and try out new things. And don't worry about slip-ups. Life would be fairly joyless without the occasional naughty treat. As long as your diet is 80 per cent healthy, you can do what you like with the other 20 per cent!

It's also worth considering the issue of food allergies and intolerance. Keep a food diary to detect correlations between your attacks and the foods you eat. There is no doubt that food allergies and sensitivities may trigger panic or anxiety attacks.

## The Quick-fix 'Solutions'

Alcohol and smoking are often used to provide instant relaxation, and to take our minds off events and pressures at hand. There is ample research, however, that both of these quick fixes actually do a lot more harm than good in the context of panic attacks. What's more, both put pressure on the body, which undermines good health on every level. If you can stick to the recommended one drink a day, you will be within safe limits and may actually benefit from the gently relaxing effect. Any more than this, however, and you are likely to suffer ill-effects, including strain on the liver (which is required to balance blood sugar levels and adrenaline).

Studies show that smoking causes the blood vessels to restri
which makes relaxation nearly impossible. Experts suggest that
there is one single thing that you can do to feel less stressed an
more relaxed, it is to give up smoking.

Finally, it's worth noting that severely depressed or anxious peo
ple are at high risk for alcoholism, smoking, and other forms
addiction.

## Do You Need Supplements?

Ideally, a balanced, healthy diet contains foods that are good natur
sources of all the nutrients we need. However, vitamins are easi
destroyed by canning, processing, refining and even cooking. Mine
als are not necessarily present in foods – the quality of the soil ar
the geological conditions of the area in which they were grown pla
an important part in determining the mineral content of food. Ever
balanced diet may be lacking in essential minerals or trace elemen
because of the soil in which the food was grown. There's pretty stron
evidence that intensive farming robs soil of its nutrient conten
which means that our food is, naturally, lower in minerals than
should be.

Secondly, and perhaps most importantly, our modern, ove
scheduled lives place demands on our bodies which cause the
to require extra nutrients. Pollution, noise, stress, food additiv
and many other factors combine to put stress on the body. Stre
of any kind – whether it is emotional or physical – increases o
need for nutrients.

## What Do We Need?
● Everyone will benefit from essential fatty acids (EFAs), now da
gerously deficient in our diets. Try flaxseed oil (dribbled on foo
or whizzed in the blender with orange juice), which is high in cr
cial Omega-3 oils. Essential fatty acids are converted into sul
stances that keep our blood thin, lower blood pressure, decrea
inflammation, improve the function of our nervous and immur
systems, help insulin to work, affect our vision, improve our co
ordination and mood, encourage healthy metabolism and mair
tain the balance of water in our bodies. Evening primrose oi
pumpkin seed oil and borage oil are also good sources of EFA

A shortage of EFAs has been linked to stress: a deficiency exacerbates symptoms and makes it harder to cope with stressors, while stress itself sets up conditions in which our bodies actually require more EFAs.

If you suffer from recurrent infections (colds, coughs and ear infections), make sure that you take extra vitamin C, which helps to boost the immune system. Constant, low-grade infections are a sign of stress and an indication that the immune system is not functioning at optimum level. Give it a boost. There's also evidence that vitamin C has a positive impact on panic attacks (see page 76).

With iron-deficiency anaemia on the increase, it may be necessary to supplement iron. Most good vitamin and mineral tablets contain iron.

Stress reduces many nutrients in our bodies – in particular, the B vitamins. If you are experiencing stress of any kind, it's a good idea to increase your intake. B vitamins work together, so don't try supplementing any one at a time, unless recommended by a nutritionist. Once again, a good multi-vitamin and -mineral tablet should adequately cover the B vitamins.

Everyone needs antioxidants, which help to reduce the onset of degenerative diseases and which are now known to have cancer-preventing qualities. The main antioxidants are vitamins A, C and E, and the minerals zinc and selenium. Make sure these appear in your multi-vitamin, or look for antioxidant tablets. Ultimately, the antioxidants are the nutrients that will help to undo some of the damage done by emotional, physical and environmental stress, fear and panic. Zinc, in particular, is crucial for anyone under pressure. It's needed for cell repair, efficient digestion, immune function and emotional health. What's more, zinc is required for the production of the adrenal hormones, which means that what little you get in your diet will probably be zapped up by the stress response. About a third of all adults do not get even the minimum suggested requirement of zinc.

## Cut the Caffeine

A new study shows that caffeine increases stress levels. Caffein overstimulates the adrenal glands, which might appear to *help* stre levels, but in the long term will reduce your ability to cope with pre sure. Even a moderate amount of caffeine raises levels of the stre hormones adrenaline and cortisol to levels higher than those no mally produced during a stress reaction. Caffeine also prevents th absorption of some essential nutrients, particularly zinc and B vit mins.

According to research, drinking four or five cups of coffee a d makes the body act as if it is under constant stress. Combined wi other stresses, it can increase blood pressure significantly, leadir to an increased risk of long-term heart disease. A study of 72 regul coffee drinkers by researchers at the Duke University Medical Cent in North Carolina found that they produced high levels of adrenalir and noradrenaline hormones. Professor James Lane, who took pa in the research, says: 'Moderate caffeine consumption makes a pe son react like he or she is having a very stressful day. If you combir the effects of real stress with the artificial boost in stress hormon that comes from caffeine, then you have compounded the effec considerably.'

Over a two-week period, the coffee drinkers' adrenaline leve increased by 32 per cent, with a 14 per cent rise in noradrenalir levels. Their blood pressure rose by an average three points. The ho mone levels remained high until night-time, even when coffee w last consumed before 1 p.m. Professor Lane says that a regul boost of three points in blood pressure could contribute to lon term health problems. Studies have shown that a rise of five poin in diastolic blood pressure – the bottom number in blood pressu readings – can increase the risk of stroke by 34 per cent and th chance of suffering a heart attack by 21 per cent.

## Exercise

It's an obvious one, but exercise is all too scarce in the modern lif style. Not only is exercise crucial for overall health, but it dramatical affects well-being. For one thing, it is well established that exercis reduces stress. One study in particular claims that regular exercis an reduce it dramatically. During periods of high stress, those who ·ported exercising less frequently had 37 per cent more physical ymptoms than their counterparts who exercised more often. In ddition, highly stressed people who get less exercise report 21 per ent more anxiety than those who exercise more frequently. Exercise ·orks by using up the adrenaline that is created by stress and stress-ıl situations. It also creates endorphins, the feel-good hormones ıat improve mood, motivation and even tolerance of pain and ther stimuli.

Exercise is good for the brain. Aerobic exercise helps to increase ıe number of brain chemicals, called neurotransmitters, so that ıessages can be carried more quickly over brain cells. This increases ıental flexibility and agility over longer periods of time, and affects motional health. Furthermore, regular exercise increases the sup-·ly of oxygenated blood to the brain, which can improve concentra-on, alertness and intellectual capacity. All of these are diminished ı periods of stress and panic, so it's worth ensuring optimum perfor-ıance by establishing a good exercise routine.

Regular exercise can promote good, regular sleeping habits. What's nore, it is now linked with self-esteem and mental attitude. Regular xercise produces muscle strength, gains in aerobic fitness, feelings ·f control over the environment and positive feedback from friends, ·hich can make us feel better about ourselves. What's more, a fit per-on tends to have their weight under control, which improves ıppearance and self-image. Finally, exercise may help to clear your nind of worrying thoughts and anxieties, and can encourage more ·roblem-solving.

Try to get at least three one-hour sessions per week. Go for exercise hat promotes flexibility, builds muscle, and gives the heart and lungs ı good work-out (aerobic) and makes them stronger. That doesn't nean heading down to the gym every night. The majority of these ıeeds can be met by brisk walking, a game of football with your chil-lren in the park, a tennis match with your friends, or even an inten-ive housecleaning session!

## Sleep

The relationship between sleep and well-being cannot be over-exag-gerated. A sleep deficit will exacerbate feelings of being out of control

– and, in fact, all of the emotional symptoms of stress. It will als
compromise immunity and the efficiency of your body. It is essenti
that you feel rested and relaxed in order successfully to combat ar
control panic attacks. If you are underslept and jittery, you are muc
more likely to succumb.

Sleep is not only important for overall health, but it is essential fo
ensuring that your body is working at optimum level and that you ar
physically and emotionally able to cope with the demands of day-to
day living. Unfortunately, sleep problems are often associated wit
panic disorder, which is a difficult case scenario. Obviously, if yo
fear having a nocturnal attack, you will sleep less well, and perhap
even fear sleeping. However, lack of sleep means that you will be les
physically and emotionally equipped to cope with panic.

Sleep gives your body time to recharge its batteries, enabling ti
sue repair and cell growth to take place. During sleep, many diffe
ent hormones are also released and, given that hormone imbalanc
is undoubtedly at the root of some cases of panic attacks, this i
important.

## Getting a Good Night's Sleep

1. Avoid any stimulants such as tea, coffee, sugar and chocolat
   during the day, which affect blood sugar levels and promot
   the release of adrenaline.
2. Make sure that you are eating little and often during the day t
   keep your blood sugar levels steady.
3. If you regularly wake in the middle of the night – especially
   you wake abruptly and with palpitations – have a small snac
   of complex carbohydrates, such as an oat cake, or half a slice c
   wheat or rye bread, about an hour before bedtime. This will sto
   your blood sugar dropping overnight, and prevent adrenalin
   from being released into the bloodstream to try and correct thi
   imbalance.
4. Have a cup of chamomile tea before bed, which will encourag
   relaxation.
5. Try to exercise early in the day. Exercise can be enormously sti
   mulating, and some people may find it difficult to sleep follow
   ing a late session.
6. Consider using aromatherapy oils such as bergamot, lavende
   roman chamomile and marjoram in a warm bath, just befor

bed. Avoid a hot bath, which can be stimulating, but ensure that it's warm enough to encourage relaxation. A few drops of aromatherapy oils on your pillow at bedtime, or used in a vaporiser, can have the same effect. A pre-bed, gentle massage with the same oils will help to encourage sleep.

Keep to a sleep routine, if possible setting your alarm for the same time each day. The body seems to work best when there is a sound sleep routine, waking at the same time and going to bed at the same time.

At least an hour before bed, write yourself a 'to do' list, to avoid lying in bed mulling over what needs to be done next day.

Herbs can be extremely helpful for sleep-related problems. Hops, valerian, passionflower and skullcap all work as gentle sedatives and can help you to overcome insomnia. Try not to rely on only one herb – instead, rotate among several, to ensure that you don't become overly dependent on any one herb. Chamomile is another useful sedative, as it helps to calm and tone the nervous system, promoting restful sleep.

0. Magnesium, which is known as 'nature's tranquilliser', is good for helping with sleep problems. If you suffer from restless legs or cramps, take both magnesium (250 mg per day) and vitamin E (300 iu per day).

## Relaxation and Leisure

Over the past few years the importance of leisure has become increasingly recognised, and many people now choose to spend more money on leisure pursuits than they have in the past, probably in an attempt to balance the effects of an extremely stressful lifestyle.

The word *leisure* is derived from the Latin word *licere*, which means 'to have permission'. The main reason so many people do not have enough leisure is that they are not giving themselves permission to make the time to enjoy it.

Recreation makes you feel better about yourself – more fulfilled, more satisfied, more interested and more engaged in the world outside that of your own personal experiences and concerns. Recreation comes in infinite varieties. It is often not restful in that it can be quite demanding and even exhausting (playing football or squash; cooking for friends), but it is a source of pleasure and satisfaction and a

chance to extend your skills. If it is truly recreational, it should b
markedly different from your work routine, or from the source c
your stress. If the stresses come mostly from your office, then cookir
on the weekend could be recreational, but not if constantly providir
for the family is itself a source of stress.

Hobbies are normally recreational. They give you an added intere
and often bring you into contact with like-minded people. If they ar
to serve their purpose, they should be kept free from trouble an
strife. Everyone needs this type of recreation, which may be creativ
or contemplative, social or solitary.

Furthermore, studies show that hobbies or leisure that involv
other people provide a type of social support, which can be benef
cial in stress-reduction even if the stressful situation can remain
unchanged. One study proved that people with fewer communit
ties were significantly more likely to die at a given age than thos
who had strong ties.

No one would expect a rugby player to play an entire game withou
taking breaks. Surprisingly, though, many otherwise rational peopl
think nothing of working from dawn to dusk without taking time ou
and then wonder why they become stressed. The two major issue
are pacing and the work/leisure balance.

## Pacing

Pacing has two components: monitoring your stress and energ
levels, and then pacing yourself accordingly. It is about awarenes
and vigilance: knowing when to extend yourself and when to eas
up. It is also about acting on the information your body gives you
The following important points will help you to understand this con
cept.

Increased stress produces increased performance, initially. Onc
you pass a certain point, however, any more stress results i
decreased performance. Trying harder at this point is unproductive
even counterproductive. The only sensible move is to take a break. W
need a certain amount of stress to function well (healthy tension) -
this is called *eustress* (good stress). However, stress becomes harmfu
(distress) when there is too much, when it lasts too long, or when i
occurs too often.

One of the first symptoms of distress is fatigue, which we tend tc
ignore. Cardiologist Dr Peter Nixon advocates a healthy respect fo

tigue and doing something about it before it becomes exhaustion. The other key to pacing is taking periodic time-outs. Too many people go far too long without breaks. In his book *The 20-Minute Break*, author Dr Ernest L. Rossi wrote that, just as we all have cycles of deep sleep and dream sleep throughout the night (at roughly 90- to 120-minute intervals), we also have cycles throughout the day (peaks of energy and concentration interspersed with troughs of low energy and inefficiency). These cycles are called 'ultradian rhythms' because they happen many times per day (as opposed to the 25-hour circadian rhythm with which we are all familiar). The main point of Dr Rossi's book is that we need to watch for these troughs and take 20-minute 'ultradian healing breaks' when they occur, as opposed to working through them and building up stress.

It is not always convenient for people to take time-outs when nature tells us to, but we can all become better at this. A mid-morning break, lunch, a mid-afternoon break and supper divide the day into roughly two-hour segments. These time-outs can include power naps, meditation, daydreaming, a social interlude, a short walk, a refreshment break, a change to low-concentration tasks or listening to music. It is a good investment of time that pays itself back quickly in increased productivity and reduced stress.

## The Work-Leisure Balance

Despite all our labour-saving devices, leisure is still an elusive commodity for most people. Statistics show that the average Westerner is working an extra three hours per week, which adds up to an extra month of work each year. Add to that the phenomenon of the two-career family (which makes family and leisure time even more scarce) and you start to get a picture of society on an accelerating treadmill.

Leisure time and levels of distress are inversely proportional – the less leisure, the more stress. Stress-reduction experts ask patients to fill in a chart to see what their work/leisure ratio looks like. They are asked to think of their lives (excluding sleep time) in four compartments (work, family, community and self) and then to assess what percentage of their time and energy in an average week goes into each part. There is no 'normal' range, but there is cause for concern when work is over 60 per cent and/or when self is less than 10 per cent. We all require time to meet our own needs (self-care, self-nurturing, etc.)

and when that is neglected, trouble usually follows. Self-directed acti-ities can include exercise or recreation, relaxation, socialising, enter-tainment and hobbies.

## Creativity

Dr Ellen J. Langer, a professor of psychology at Harvard Universit-calls everyday creativity 'mindfulness'. Everyday creativity or min-fulness is good for your health and well-being. It is so essential our existence that the newness, surprise and variety provided creativity actually fuel our will to live. Furthermore, art therapis-claim that spontaneous use of creativity heals the mind and bod-improving well-being by going right to the source of the problen They claim that creativity allows you to work out problems physical and creatively, without continually going over them in your min Feelings, thoughts, emotions, worries and fantasies that are exper-enced in the mind can be expressed externally through creativ effort.

If you have chosen to express your creativity in a particular mec-ium, such as paint or song, learn as much about the medium as po sible. Start slowly, practise in your medium regularly, and gai familiarity with your strengths and weaknesses. As your knowledg and skill increase, your ability to manipulate your chosen medium express your creativity will expand.

## Other Ways of Making Changes

Part of a healthy lifestyle is finding a balance, and facing up to pro blems and concerns. In the context of panic attacks, there are som very useful strategies that can be adopted to ensure that your lifesty is balanced and that you are able to put your fears and even you attacks into perspective.

Try some of the following:

● Write about your feelings. Over a dozen studies have shown that you write about your problems and concerns, you can help reliev stress, improve your immunity, make fewer visits to the docto and have a more optimistic view of life. Spending 20 minutes day writing about your deepest thoughts and feelings can encou rage a sense of relief and a release from stress.

Try a 'worry hour' where you do all of your worrying at once. Set aside an hour of every day, at roughly the same time each day. Give yourself some space and quiet, and then go for it. Consider all your deepest concerns, feelings and fears, and think them through. Write them down. Make lists. Write potential solutions. At the end of the hour, throw it all away. If you feel worried at any other time of the day, remind yourself that you can't engage in worrying until X hour!

Keep a panic diary. We discussed this concept on page 47, and it unquestionably helps to keep a documented record of triggers, feelings, symptoms and what methods help you. Report the occurrences of the anxiety attack and any thoughts and events associated with it. As you begin to perceive what underlies your anxiety, you can begin to substitute new ways of coping. The essential goal is to understand the realities of an anxiety-provoking situation and to respond with new actions based on reasonable expectations. If nothing else, it helps you to keep things in perspective.

Remind yourself of how you were before the panic set in. Make a list of the best times of your life. Look at old photos, home cinefilms and letters to jog your memory. What were you doing then that you're not taking the time to do now? How can you re-create your happy times? How did you feel on a day-to-day basis? Now is the time to make some changes.

## Relaxing

For many people, relaxation means hitting a golf ball, a couple of hours in the gym, or a vigorous game of squash. But while these activities can be stress-relieving, they can also trigger competition and frustration, two things that can actually make it harder to relax. Research shows that most people don't reach a relaxed physiological state when they are doing things that society generally considers relaxing, such as reading a newspaper, playing sports or watching television. The only real way to get into a relaxed physiological state is to let your mind go into neutral.

Experts recommend that we all take several 'mental rest stops' during the day, in order to lessen anxiety and help let go of stress and tension. This physiological state, called the relaxation

response, has been shown to lower heart rate, blood pressure a
breath rate, slow the metabolism and brain waves, and foster fe
ings of peace and tranquillity.

Occasionally relaxation or a feeling of ease and well-being ari
naturally, such as after a long, enjoyable run or a good laugh. B
the act of trying to relax when you feel stressed can be frustratin
upsetting and almost impossible. To unwind, you actually need
concentrate or focus your attention on your breathing, or on son
other sensation that will allow your mind to settle into an inhere
sense of stillness.

There are many, many ways to relax, as described in Chapt
Four, and it's essential that you adopt as many as you can. T
yoga, which will improve your fitness at the same time, or mal
time in your day for some meditation or visualisation. You do
need hours in order to relax; you simply need to find a little tin
and space for a bit of peace and respite from the rest of the worl
When you find this within yourself, you can draw upon it, or visit
whenever you feel panic coming on.

## Feel Good about Yourself

Studies show that people suffering from panic attacks suffer fro
low self-esteem and have a poor self-image. In order to feel well c
every level, it's crucial that you address these issues and learn t
develop self-awareness and, more importantly, self-love. Conf
dence and self-esteem do wonders for our minds. They provide a bu
fer against anxiety and relieve feelings of guilt, hopelessness an
inadequacy. They also give us the courage to fulfil our dreams, and
willingness to try new things, meet new challenges and overcom
difficulties.

Here are some of the best ways to feel better about yourself:

● Make sure you are in a job you like. There is nothing more destruc
tive than spending the best part of your day doing something yo
dislike. Chances are that you will not be fulfilled, and this type c
negative emotion tends to spill over into other areas of your life
Change is a good, positive step, and doing something for yourse
will kickstart the healing process.

Surround yourself with friends who like you. Many of us hang on to old acquaintances or spend time with people with whom we have little natural rapport. A healthy interaction with a few good friends is enormously stress-relieving and uplifting. Talking undoubtedly diffuses anxiety, and you need friends that you can trust to get down to the nitty-gritty. More important, however, is having friends who really like and admire you. Spend an hour one evening in a 'feel-good' session. Gather together your closest friends and ask everyone to write something positive – what they most like or admire – about every person there. Put them all into a hat and hand them out to each person. You might be surprised by how others perceive you. Keep your 'post' and read it when you are feeling insecure.

Get a new haircut, buy some clothes, or start a fitness regime. Everything you do for yourself has the effect of nurturing your self-esteem. If you look good, you'll feel good. And these feelings will all work together to promote a stronger and more positive self-image.

Take some time out. If you're running on empty, you will be neither productive nor happy. Take time to recharge. Light some scented candles, take a bath. Take a day off work. Get a massage, take singing lessons, read a great thriller. Indulge yourself. Have one glass of wine or a great meal out. Continually ask yourself what gives you pleasure, and then give it to yourself. Above all, don't feel guilty. This type of activity is incredibly uplifting, and will leave you feeling fit to face the world. Make time-outs a regular occurrence in your life. Book them into your calendar in advance, and make sure you take them!

Be positive. Use positive self-talk and positive affirmations (see page 78). Don't give up or accept defeat before you have tried. You *can* make changes. You can feel good again. You can like yourself enough to do this. Gag your internal critic. People with low self-esteem tend to hear little voices in their heads telling them: 'you can't,' 'you'll fail,' 'you're weak,' 'you're worthless.' Whenever your critical internal voice begins to put you down, silence it immediately. Be aware of the times it's most likely to appear, such as when you are feeling down. Tell yourself over and over again that you are strong, capable and worthy until the voice goes away. The same rules apply for external critics, too!

- Set some goals. Setting unrealistic goals is one way to lead to fail
  ure, which can take a toll on your self-esteem. But setting a worth
  goal, something realistic and achievable, will do wonders for you
  confidence. When you've mastered one goal, move on to the nex
  Find success at one level and then transfer it up to the next.
- Don't fear failure. Remember that failure is an opportunity for ne
  success. Life is a trial-and-error process, and we don't make ar
  progress if we don't take chances in the face of failure. And pu
  them into perspective. Most of the actual 'failures' that we exper
  ence are not nearly as harmful as the damage we do to ourselve
  when we worry about them, and plan for potential failures 1
  come. If we don't take risks, we never make changes, and w
  never have the opportunity to succeed. Take failure in your strid
  Remember the worst case scenario (see page 93). It's never as ba
  as you think it's going to be.
- Choose to be successful. Everything we do in life involve
  choices. Choose success and believe in yourself.

# Chapter Seven

# Top Ten Tips for Coping with Panic

1. Don't expect change to happen overnight. Expect to experience some anxiety and a few relapses before you get things under control. But remember: You *can* do it, and you will.

2. When you feel panic rising, wait. Breathe from your diaphragm, begin to use some positive self-talk and try to visualise a place of calm, away from it all. Watch the fear rise, and let it fall. Notice that it comes in waves. It's more than likely that you have panicked at the first waves of panic. This time, give yourself a chance to see it abate.

3. Each experience teaches you that you can actually function with discomfort. Experiencing anxiety gives you the opportunity to practise coping with it. Try to function with the fear – every success will make you stronger in the future, and your attacks less frequent and intense.

4. Learn to relax and learn to breathe. If you master these techniques you'll feel more confident about coping in future, and you will feel more in control. What's more, the new 'relaxed' you will be less likely to suffer from panic attacks at all.

5. Take advantage of the treatments available. There are literally hundreds of different treatment options, some of which have been discussed in this book. Apart from drug therapies, almost all are nurturing and healing on many levels. If you are in good physical and emotional health, you are much less likely to suffer from panic and fear.

6. Shape up. Look after your body by eating well, drinking alcohol only moderately, cutting down on caffeine, and stopping smoking. Get some exercise, ensure that you are getting enough

sleep, and take time out to do the things in life that you want to do. Your health will improve, and with that, your approach to life.

7.  Nurture yourself. Self-esteem and confidence are crucial to overcoming panic attacks, and if you feel good about yourself you will be much less likely to succumb. It may seem trite, particularly if you have been suffering for many years, but a strong self-image creates self-belief and power. If you can overpower the fear, you will be free from panic attacks for ever.

8.  Learn some on-the-spot coping techniques. If you have a battery of means by which you can deal with a panic attack when it hits, you'll feel much less frightened of them and they will naturally become less frequent. Remember that fear breeds fear and, in this case, panic attacks. If you know that you have some tried-and-tested techniques to hand, you will get through the attacks more easily. The confidence that success brings will draw an end to the episodes.

9.  Don't be afraid to ask for help. Talk to your doctor and your friends; join a support group. Sharing a problem puts it into perspective and offers emotional release. The love and support of friends, family and colleagues will also boost your self-image and fear is never as overwhelming when you know there is help to hand.

10. Know that you can cope and you will. Remember that your body is letting you down in a panic attack. Go with it, relax into it, and don't be tempted to run away. Research has shown that if someone leaves a situation while in a state of panic or high anxiety, they have more difficulty returning the next time. Weather the storm, and resolve to make this panic attack your very last.

# Further Reading

**Books**

Roger Baker, *Understanding Panic Attacks and Overcoming Fear* (Lion Publishing, 1995)

Nikki Bradford and Karen Sullivan *et al.*, *The Hamlyn Encyclopaedia of Complementary Health* (Hamlyn, 1997)

Koz Christopher *et al.*, *No Need to Fear: Overcoming Panic Disorder* (CreativeWorks Publishing, 2001)

Carol Goldman and Shirley Babior, *Overcoming Panic, Anxiety and Phobias: New Strategies to Free Yourself from Worry and Fear* (Whole Person Associates, 1995)

Kevin Gournay, *No Panic: A Practical Guide to Managing Panic and Phobia* (Asset Books, 1996)

Christine Ingham, *Panic Attacks* (HarperCollins, 2000)

Susan Jeffers, *Feel the Fear and Do It Anyway* (Rider, 1997)

Alice Neville, *Who's Afraid ...? Coping with Fear, Anxiety and Panic Attacks* (Arrow Books, 1991)

Jennifer Shoquist and Diane Stafford, *No More Panic Attacks: A 30-Day Plan for Conquering Anxiety* (New Page Books, 2001)

Derrick Silove and Vijaya Manicavasagar, *Overcoming Panic: A Self-Help Guide Using Cognitive Behavioral Techniques* (New York University Press, 2001)

Karen Sullivan, *How to Cope Successfully with ... Your Lifestyle Diet* (Wellhouse Publishing, 2002)

**Audio Cassettes**

Albert Smith MNAHP, MNCP, *No More Panic Attacks* (Albert Smith Health Cassettes, 1995)

# Useful Resources

## Alcohol and Smoking

ALCOHOLICS ANONYMOUS (AA)
www.alcoholics-anonymous.org.uk

ASH (Action on Smoking and Health)
www.ash.org.uk

## Allergies

ALLERGY UK
www.allergyuk.org

BRITISH SOCIETY FOR ALLERGY & CLINICAL IMMUNOLOGY
www.bsaci.org

BRITISH SOCIETY FOR ALLERGY,
ENVIRONMENT AND NUTRITIONAL MEDICINE
www.jnem.demon.co.uk

## Emotional and Psychological Help

MIND
(National Assciation for Mental Health)
www.mind.org.uk

YOUNG MINDS
www.youngminds.org.uk

# ComplementaryTherapies

BRITISH ACUPUNCTURE COUNCIL
www.acupuncture.org.uk

BRITISH HOMEOPATHIC ASSOCIATION
www.britishhomeopathic.org

BRITISH HYPNOTHERAPY ASSOCIATION
www.hypnotherapy-association.org

THE BRITISH REFLEXOLOGY ASSOCIATION
www.britreflex.co.uk

BRITISH WHEEL OF YOGA
1 Hamilton Place
Boston Road,
Sleaford,
Lincolnshire NG34 7ES

GENERAL COUNCIL AND REGISTER OF NATUROPATHS
www.naturopathy.org.uk

INSTITUTE OF COMPLEMENTARY AND NATURAL MEDICINE (ICM)
www.i-c-m.org.uk

INTERNATIONAL FEDERATION OF PROFESSIONAL AROMAHERAPISTS
www.ifparoma.org

INTERNATIONAL FEDERATION FOR VIBRATIONAL MEDICINE
Tel: 01963 23468/23774

NATIONAL INSTITUTE OF MEDICAL HERBALISTS
www.nimh.org.uk

SOCIETY OF HOMEOPATHS
www.homeopathy-soh.org

## Emotional and Psychological Help

MIND (National Association for Mental Health)
www.mind.org.uk

YOUNG MINDS
www.youngminds.org.uk

## Flower Essenses

BRITISH FLOWER AND VIBRATIONAL ESSENC ASSOCIATION (BFVEA)
www.bfvea.com

THE DR EDWARD BACH CENTRE
www.bachcentre.com

INTERNATIONAL FEDERATION OF VIBRATIONAL MECICINE
01963 23038

## Nutritional Help

BRITISH NUTRITION FOUNDATION
www.nutrition.org.uk

INSTITUTE OF OPTIMUM NUTRITION
www.ion.ac.uk

ANXIETY ZONE
www.anxietyzone.com

INTERNATIONAL STRESS MANAGEMENT ASSOCIATION (ISMA)
www.isma.org.uk

ROYAL COLLEGE OF PSYCHIATRISTS
www.rcpsych.ac.uk

UK Council for Psychotherapy
www.psychotherapy.org.uk

# Index

HOW TO COPE SUCCESSFULLY WITH

# HIGH BLOOD PRESSURE

### Dr Duncan Dymond

Blood Pressure is not a disease, everyone has a pressure, we need it to keep us upright and alive. Your blood pressure varies depending on your level of physical and mental stress. In this easily accessible book Dr Dymond describes what high blood pressure is, the symptoms, various medications available, side effects and possible complications. The tests and investigations for high blood pressure are explained together with treatments and suggestions for changes to lifestyle and diet.

ISBN: 1-903784-07-7       128pp

HOW TO COPE SUCCESSFULLY WITH

# ANXIETY AND DEPRESSION

### Beth MacEoin

We live in stressful times and have to cope on a daily basis with a variety of different pressures. These can include financial worries, emotional stresses, bereavement, break-up of relationships and insecurity at work. When feeling well and resilient we are able to cope with a wide range of these stressful situations. It is when we become mentally and emotionally overloaded at a vulnerable time in our lives that we can suffer from symptoms of anxiety or depression. Beth MacEoin describes in her easily accessible style the various symptoms and suggests a wide range of practical measures to provide positive support.

ISBN: 1-903784-03-4       128pp

HOW TO COPE SUCCESSFULLY WITH

# IRRITABLE BOWEL SYNDROME

Richard Emerson

Irritable Bowel Syndrome is a complex problem with both physical and psychological symptoms. The aim of this book is to set out clearly and concisely these symptoms and the various treatments now available – conventional, complementary and alternative. Ths should enable sufferers to improve their lifestyle and either cure or manage their Irritable Bowel Syndrome.

ISBN: 1-903784-06-9

128pp

HOW TO COPE SUCCESSFULLY WITH

# DIVERTICULITIS

Dr Joan McClelland

Diverticulitis is a Cinderella disorder. It is very common, can be dangerous and there are rapidly increasing numbers of sufferers. We stand a more than 50 per cent chance of suffering from diverticulitis before we reach the age of 60. Dr Joan McClelland describes in her easily accessible style the symptoms, different types of diverticulitis, complications and various treatments including alternative and herbal remedies. This book also covers the psychological aspects of diverticulitis and the benefits of exercise and diet.

ISBN: 1-903784-00-X

128pp

# THYROID PROBLEMS

## Dr Tom Smith

The thyroid is not a subject that immediately springs to mind when we chat socially about our health. We marvel how some people have boundless energy while others are always tired and weary. There are nervous, anxious, agitated people who can never sit still. It is easy to assume that people differ in these ways because of their characters or lifestyle but a substantial number have developed these characteristics through no fault of their own. These are the sufferers from thyroid problems. Do Tom Smith describes in his easily accessible style the symptoms, different types of thyroid problems, complications and the various treatments available today.

ISBN: 1-903784-01-8                                          128pp

# YOUR LIFESTYLE DIET

## Karen Sullivan

A healthy diet is more than just balancing food intake, it involves eating foods that promote rather than endanger health. What are the elements of a healthy balanced diet? How do we identify which are good fats, bad fats and essential fats? What problems can be caused by sugar in our diet? What are the different types of sugars found in our diet and which are healthy? What should we drink and what should we avoid drinking? What essential supplements do we need? The answers to these questions and many more are contained in Your Lifestyle Diet.

ISBN: 1-903784-04-2                                          128pp

# NO DIET WEIGHT LOSS

### Pat Walder

- Have you tried of an endless variety of diets?
- Do you find you lose some weight, then put it all back on again plus a little more?
- Do you envy those people who can eat whatever they like and never put on weight?
- If you answered yes to any, or all, of the above questions, then what is contained within the pages **No Diet Weight Loss** will solve all your problems. This is a radical new way of achieving your perfect body weight and maintaining that weight PERMANENTLY – without diets, pills, potions or excessive exercise.

**Dr Tom Smith** said about this book:-

'This book is full of common sense and good advice on how to change one's life permanently to overcome all the habits that produce obesity. I will certainly recommend it to my patients. It gives people an excellent insight into themselves and how they have become overweight. It gives rational and sound advice on how to change their attitudes and lifestyle, not just so that they can be thinner, but happier with themselves, too. And it does this in a style that is easy to read, with humour and sympathy. An excellent book for everyone involved in obesity – and nowadays that means more than half of the adult population. I wish I had written it myself.'

ISBN 1-903784-10-7

96pp + CD